PIGEONS, DOVES AND DOVECOTES

by

M. D. L. Roberts and V. E. Gale

Edited and Illustrated by

Sara Roadnight

Photographs by

Michael Roberts

PUBLISHED BY GOLD COCKEREL BOOKS
ISBN 0947870-31-8

PIGEONS, DOVES AND DOVECOTES

CONTENTS

INTRODUCTION

This book is aimed at the person who wants to keep a few doves or pigeons in a wallcote, a polecote or an aviary. It does not tell you how to keep and race pigeons, or raise squabs commercially.

We have tried to explain every aspect of keeping doves, their management, feeding, breeding, sexing and what can befall them, so that the newcomer is not daunted by the prospect of having a few birds; however we have pointed out the realities as well.

Sara had always wanted to keep a few white garden fantails, and of course I rose to the challenge of housing them in the most pleasing and convenient way when they arrived.

Our knowledge of keeping doves was scant compared with Stormy Gale's; he has come to the rescue in helping us to write this book and passing on the years of experience he has gained in breeding many different sorts of pigeon for his own interest since he was a boy. He currently breeds Voorburg Shield Croppers, a type of pouting pigeon which he bought from Charles Mayhew 20 years ago.

We are both very grateful for his contribution, and hope that this book will be of interest not only to the beginner but also to the more experienced breeder.

MICHAEL ROBERTS & SARA ROADNIGHT
KENNERLEIGH, DEVON - MARCH 2000

4

BREEDS OF DOMESTIC PIGEON

In subsequent chapters the history of the relationship between man and the pigeon will be traced, from the common Rock Pigeon/Dove, through untold generations to over 400 different types or breeds which have evolved to meet the needs and fancies of man today. There are many excellent, well illustrated books describing the tremendous variation in size, shape, colour and habits of modern domestic pigeons.

Where the emphasis has been on the selection of pigeons for the table, large breeds of around 2lbs in weight such as the Kings (USA), the Carneau (France) and the Mondains (Italy) have been developed. But the largest, strangely called the "Runt", can weigh 3lbs or more.

At the other end of the scale are the small, exquisite, frilled and muffed Satinetts, Turbits and other Oriental Frills sometimes called "toy" breeds,

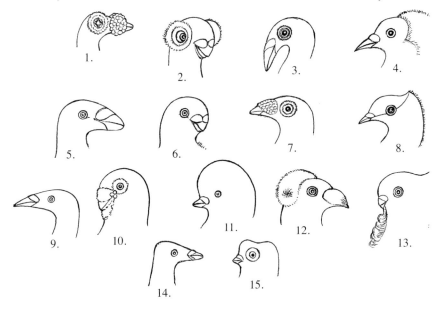

1. English Carrier   2. Barb   3. Bagdad   4. Montauban
5. Antwerp   6. English Owl   7. Dragoon   8. Mookee
9. Magpie   10. Flamenca Runt   11. English Long-Faced Tumbler
12. German Double-Crested Trumpeter   13. Blondinettes   14. Exhibition Homer
15. Vienna Short-Faced Tumbler

where breeders have concentrated on feathering and colour. In between, there are the medium sized birds where posture and display have received priority, as in the Fantails, Pouters and unusually hooded Jacobins.

Next there are the strong flying breeds where different flight characteristics have been encouraged; examples are the Tumblers and Rollers which literally "tumble" or perform back somersaults in flight, apparently for the sheer joy of it, and the Tipplers which have been trained to circle in the air above their home for hours on end, showing amazing endurance until called down.

Lastly there is the way the homing instinct has been developed in certain strains of pigeon so that they may be used as message carriers in war and peace; this is now personified in the Racing Homer.

CHOICE OF BREED

Assuming that the reader of this book does not intend to become a commercial producer of table birds or "squabs" as the young birds are called, nor does he or she aspire to venture into the field of racing pigeons, then the choice of breed will rest with the medium sized "fancy" or "display" breeds and their suitability for the type of environment and housing which can be provided.

Generally speaking all pigeons enjoy the freedom to fly where and when they will (except perhaps the Runts which seem to spend their time pecking around on the floor). However, some breeds seem to tolerate restrictions on their area of flight more readily than others. The so called "display" breeds, (Fantails are prime examples of this), will thrive just as well in an aviary where they have no more than the minimum area to cover in flight, as they would if allowed to fly free. Indeed, when free to fly they seldom get further than your neighbour's roof where they will remain, stubbornly resisting all efforts to entice them home!

The Toy breeds too are probably best suited to aviary style housing; however they also have other limitations which make some of them difficult for a beginner to manage; for example, many of the modern Toy breeds have such diminutive beaks that it is difficult for them to feed their young, therefore other breeds have to be kept as well to act as foster parents.

For our purposes then it is suggested that the choice of breed to start with should be confined to those which can be easily managed and are best suited to the small or medium sized garden where free flight may or may not be an option.

The breed chosen should also be decorative and a pleasure to look at. The following four breeds appear to meet these criteria and are therefore recommended as possibilities to be considered by anyone planning to start keeping pigeons: the Fantail because it has the most eye catching style, carriage, and colour too, if required; the Nun with its very distinctive markings and adaptability to any conditions; the Voorburg with its elegant pouter-like stance which also has distinctive markings and is adaptable to management variations; and finally the Modena, a stocky, perky, neat breed, available in a multitude of colour combinations.

To this list could be added Tumblers and/or Rollers, especially where there are no restrictions on flight. However, there are so many variations in type, size, colour and flight behaviour within this group that it is best to leave these to the more experienced pigeon keepers.

A brief description of the four breeds recommended with colour illustrations follows:

Force-feeding a pigeon, taken from a bas-relief circa 2,500 BC.

1) The Fantail is certainly one of the most attractive and popular of all breeds. It seems almost tailor made for gardens both in its exotic appearance and the general air of calm it gives as it flutters rather than flies from A to B. However it is in fact a very nervous breed, and birds when agitated are prone to compulsive trembling, which at one time led to them being known as "shakers". Nevertheless they are easily tamed and respond to the human voice. There are many variations in colour from plain white to solid black (very attractive, shown off by red legs and white wattles on the beak). There are also those with black or red tails or other combinations of black and white and/or red and the more usual "pigeon colours" of blues and silvers.

There are however three types of Fantail, the "Show" or exhibition type, its country cousin, commonly known as the "Garden fantail" and the "Indian". The Garden Fantail is the hardiest and most suitable for free flying. The main difference lies in the carriage of the tail which is like a fully opened fan (with 30 or more feathers as opposed to the normal 12-14), held erect in the Show type, whereas in the Garden type, the tail (with apparently fewer feathers) is only half raised and gives the impression of being half opened most of the time, which does make for easier flight. Also, when the more highly bred Show types are displaying their tails fully, they lean over backwards so far that their heads almost disappear, giving the impression of a headless bird. In this position they cannot see anyone approaching and are easy prey to cats, sparrowhawks etc. The Garden variety, although doing its best with tail displays, does not suffer those disabilities, enjoys flying, though limited in range, and is therefore easier to manage and more suited to a dovecote on a pole than the Show type or the Indian which are better kept in an aviary.

2) Nuns. A breed developed in Germany. The colouring is most distinctive with an overall white body but a well defined coloured bib and head with a full white crest. Wing and tail feathers are also coloured. Although black is the commonest colour, red, yellow and duns are equally attractive. They are medium sized active birds which are very adaptable and therefore easily managed. They enjoy free flight but without any inclination to fly too far or for too long. A flock of Nuns strutting about the lawn would enhance any garden.

3) Voorburgs. The Voorburg Shield Cropper, to give its full name, is a pouter type breed of Dutch origin. It has a basically white body with white tail and wing feathers but with coloured wing coverts, hence the "shield". A slender, upright carriage gives it a very elegant appearance and there are many different colours of the "shield" available, from black to red and yellow, with or without bars. A large well developed crop is quite striking when inflated, particularly by the male birds, but is not so over-blown as to make it look clumsy. Again, a very interesting breed to have in the garden. In addition they are equally attractive in flight, the wing colours showing up clearly as they circle and dive between the trees.

4) Modenas. Originally a highflying breed from northern Italy and named after the city of Modena. The modern breed however is not noted for its flight as it is more of a chunky compact type with a solid body and upturned tail giving it a perky amusing appearance. There are countless variations in colour but they can be divided into two groups, the Gazzi which has a white body and coloured head, wings and tail, and the Schietti type with overall body colouring in mixed colours. Certainly if colour is wanted this breed can provide it, whether in an aviary or dovecote. It is hardy, active, easy to manage, looks neat and is noted for being a good parent.

Having decided which breed or breeds you find most interesting, the best way to see them live is to attend one of the county Agricultural shows or poultry shows where there are classes for pigeons, although not all shows have them these days. You will be able to get the names and addresses of the exhibitors from the catalogue, and if you are lucky, may even be able to meet and talk to the owners of the birds you admire most. Another approach would be to contact the secretary of the Society, Association or Club of the breed in which you are interested, for information about their shows and/or the possibilities of birds for sale.

Lastly, it is advisable for the beginner to start with one breed only, for although birds tend to mate at first only with their like, sooner or later there will be too many young cocks or hens of one sort or another, and cross breeding becomes inevitable. The result, a somewhat weird mixed flock of cross breeds which no one wants.

WHERE TO BUY

Most people who buy a polecote or a wallcote want white doves to go with it. The best way to obtain these, without having to travel too far, is to ask at your local pet shop or bird and aviary specialist; you could also ask at your nearest corn and seed merchant who supplies pigeon food, or look in the livestock columns of your local newspaper.

If you want more unusual birds you need to get hold of a copy of one of the specialist pigeon papers, (a list of these is at the back of the book), or go to your local agricultural show which may have a tent exhibiting pigeons; better still, there may be a pigeon show locally. It would be worth contacting your local pigeon club or representative, as they are a close-knit group of people who are often very helpful and know who is breeding what, and they can frequently point you in the right direction.

How do I know they are young birds?

The main differences between young birds and adult birds are as follows:

a) The bill or beak of a young bird is longer and broader than that of an adult.

b) A young bird will tend to be in moult, ie it is growing its adult feathers.

c) With specialist breeds, look for the colour of the ring on the leg (see ringing).

HOUSING

One of the first pleasures involved with starting to keep pigeons is planning the design of your own pigeon house. That there has always been a strong desire for the individual pigeon owner to express himself with his own unusual design, is well demonstrated in the illustrations in another chapter of the fantastically ornate "multi-storey" dovecotes of the Middle East and Mediterranean countries. This individuality of design is also evident in the varying shapes and decorative features of those "pigeonniers" seen in France and the more solid old dovecotes found at manor houses in this country.

The most attractive design to choose is undoubtedly the dovecote on a pole type called a polecote. After all it is certainly the most spectacular way to show off your birds, it also enhances your garden and can therefore give great pleasure on both counts.

Apart from the racing pigeon loft, there are three principle methods of housing doves and pigeons for the hobbyist:

a)   The Polecote, mainly made of wood

b)   The Wallcote, this can be made of wood, but the original wallcotes were built into the sides of houses or barns.

c)   The aviary, or converted stable or garden shed.

Construction

As mentioned before, the designs of pigeon houses are legion. There are several points to look out for here: first, that the pigeons have individual nest boxes with their own entrance holes and don't have to share, which would lead to constant battles; second, that the pigeon on her nest is sheltered from the wind and rain; third, that the house is easy to clean out, particularly if you are up a ladder 8' off the ground; fourth, that the construction, if in timber, shouldn't be in plyboard, as this will delaminate in time; and fifth, if the dovecote is to be painted, white is preferable, as it does not show the pigeon droppings as much as darker colours.

POLECOTES AND WALLCOTES

Most people go out and buy a ready-made polecote or wallcote and there is a list of suppliers at the back of the book, but for those who are able and have the time, it is quite fun to design and make your own, especially in keeping with local architecture.

One of the most important factors is the maintenance of your pigeon house, not only the cleaning but painting as well. It has to be 6 - 8 ft (183 - 244 cms) off the ground to stop cats from worrying the birds, so this means access by ladder. A ladder against a wall is fine, but one against a polecote can be tricky, especially if access to the house is just through a pop hole. When I designed my pigeon house, I did so knowing that I am not very good up ladders so the insides of the house had to be easily accessible.

In my design I have got rid of the ladder climb altogether, by making the accommodation section slide up and down the pole on a winch system. There are opening doors on each side, and an area large enough for a sitting bird to get out of the wind and rain. The area inside is roughly an 18" (46 cms) triangle per bird with a height of 10" (55 cms) between each tier. The pop holes should be 3¾" to 4" wide (9½ - 10 cms) and 5½" to 6" (14 - 15 cms) high. Of course these should be tailor made depending on the breed of pigeon kept. Conversely, the pop holes should not be too large as then the pigeons will not feel safe.

Polecotes can become very heavy affairs if you have more than two tiers, so this must be taken into consideration when designing one. I have seen some really beautiful designs but it's hard to imagine how they could be cleaned; maybe they are just used as garden ornaments.

Wallcotes Many of the important points about polecotes should be taken into account when designing a wallcote. The one I designed was made with "drawers" in it so I could remove a dirty drawer without upsetting a sitting pigeon next door. However I did make two mistakes: first, I should have put partitions on the outside front between the pop holes to stop a dominant male from taking over a complete level or tier, and secondly I painted it green, which shows every pigeon dropping! White would have been a more sensible colour. Microporous "Ranch" paint is best to use. It costs more but will not blister or peel.

Simple boxes on a wall would work well, and in fact this system was used inside early dovecotes, the boxes being made of wood or clay, or baskets of willow or hazel.

Various Polecotes that can be found on the market to-day. By courtesy of Forsham Cottage Arks, Kootensaw Dovecotes & NGF Dovecotes.

Avaries, Stables and Garden Sheds

Having decided that the design will be your own, where do you start? For those who are not very architecturally minded and who will not be satisfied with anything less than their own custom built house, maybe the conversion of an old outbuilding or a simple garden shed will do. This can provide plenty of scope for an innovative approach and allows for an early start instead of having to build the whole external structure from scratch.

Generally speaking there are a few ground rules to follow. There is a tremendous variety of garden sheds on offer these days, both in design and size, not to mention quality and price. A simple apex type or a lean-to of approximately 7' x 5' (213 cms x 152 cms) is a comfortable size to work with; (anything narrower is restrictive, especially for cleaning, and for the birds too). This should also provide adequate accommodation for the 2 pairs of pigeons one is likely to start with, plus their offspring for a couple of years ahead up to a maximum of 7 to 8 pairs. If it has a wooden floor it should be supported on bricks 12" (30 cms) or more off the ground to avoid damp and the rats and mice normally attracted by the pigeon food. However, if you are sure of the site, the best precaution against rats is a concrete floor with the wooden structure mounted on a brick wall 12" or more high. Therefore, if it is possible to buy the shed you want without the floor, perhaps this might be a better option in the long run.

Good ventilation and light are important, and most sheds available at a reasonable price already have a glazed window or windows on the same side as the door. This might be adequate as far as light is concerned, but unless the window can be opened (and covered with 1" wire mesh) poor ventilation could lead to damp conditions resulting in many unnecessary problems. Alternatively you could have a half door with an additional wire netting covered top half used during the day and the more solid wooden top half closed at night. Or simply add a framed wire door on the inside of the wooden one for daily use. This would allow fresh air to enter at ground level, providing the best form of circulation. It might also be useful to have a long shelf inside, just under the window, which can be used by the birds to look out and get their bearings on their new home.

If it has been decided that the birds are (eventually) going to be free flying then pop-holes can be cut in the gable end of the shed. For pigeon breeds of the size we recommend, the pop-holes should be approximately 7" or 8" high by 4" wide (18 or 20 cms high by 10 cms wide). At least four holes are needed if all the birds are to be able to come and go freely and not be kept out by some domineering male standing guard over the entrance. There should also be a

14

landing stage on the outside and a flap internally for closing the pop-holes at night. The latter is also useful for keeping the birds shut in if you want to catch any of them.

Most garden sheds will have a felt-covered roof and in order for the pigeons to settle comfortably on it, wooden battens nailed on parallel to the ridge at about 9" -10" (23 - 26 cms) intervals, will be a great help.

If free flying is not an option then a flight area or aviary will have to be built on to whichever end of the shed is most convenient. It should be at least as big as the house, preferably twice the size or bigger if possible, and be covered with 1" wire netting which allows for plenty of fresh air and sunshine but keeps out the wild birds which come after the pigeon food. It is also useful to have a shelf at least along the long side of the area if not all the way round, for the birds to alight on and sun themselves etc. whenever they wish.

An aviary need not depend on being an extension to a house; it can be an entity on its own. It can be used to surround a box or boxes on a wall, and incorporated into the design of the garden with a gravel floor, pool and/or fountain which the pigeons will be as happy to use as other birds would. A creeper can be planted on the weather side as protection against the wind (see notes on gardens), or quick growing shrubs planted on the outside for the same purpose. Domestic pigeons do not normally want to perch on the branches of trees and shrubs which one usually sees in aviaries for other birds, so some more rigid forms of perch will have to be devised.

A franking mark from Japan showing flying pigeons.

15

AVIARY HOUSE WITH OUTSIDE VERANDA.

AVIARY HOUSE WITH OUTSIDE FLIGHT

16

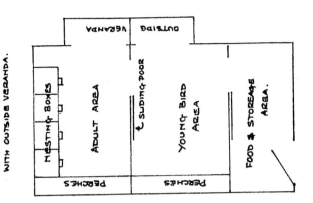

PLAN OF AVIARY HOUSE
WITH OUTSIDE VERANDA.

VERANDA   OUTSIDE

NESTING BOXES
ADULT AREA
SLIDING DOOR
YOUNG BIRD AREA
FOOD & STORAGE AREA.
PERCHES
PERCHES

PLAN OF AVIARY HOUSE WITH
OUTSIDE FLIGHT

OUTSIDE FLIGHTS
OUTSIDE FLIGHTS

NESTING BOXES
BREEDING OR ADULT AREA.
SLIDING DOOR
YOUNG BIRD AREA
FOOD & STORAGE AREA
PERCHES
PERCHES

17

INTERIORS OF AVIARIES, STABLES OR SHEDS

A simple box on the wall could be considered as a unit or module per pair of birds. Outside it can be used on its own and/or repeated side by side or above or below each other under one roof, as the flock grows. Internally likewise, in a shed or whatever structure is finally decided upon, the units can be deployed to suit the circumstances. It is suggested that each unit should measure between 20" to 24" x 18" to 20" (51-61 cms x 46-51 cms) if it is to be used for any of the four breeds that we recommend. It should have a central partition for about ⅔ its width, so that in fact it provides two nesting places per pair. All pigeons seem to prefer this to a single nest system as it allows the birds to build a second nest and possibly lay again before the first youngsters have flown. When used outside, the front of the box can be covered with wire and the space behind it used for small individual containers for food and water. This is particularly useful at the beginning when the birds must be confined until they get to know their new home. When such units or variations of it, are used within a closed shed where communal food hoppers and drinkers are provided, there is no need for a wire front. However it is always useful to have a removable front handy which can be put in place to confine a particular pair, of perhaps newly mated birds etc. It can also be used to keep any unoccupied nest boxes closed when not in use, (unless each unit can be removed until wanted) as some pairs cannot resist the temptation of "moving in next door" or worse still, incorporating "next door" into their own domain.

Nest boxes should be easy to clean and for this reason clay bowls (or basins used for pot plants) of 7" to 9" (18-23 cms) diameter are ideal for the birds to build their nests in. The old nest can then be thrown out as the youngsters leave. (Plastic bowls are hopeless, unless there is some way of stabilizing them, as they tip up whenever a bird stands on the rim). Bowls are not imperative however, and a small strip of wood nailed across the partition to keep the nest in place is a common alternative (see diagram).

Enthusiasts who breed for shows or for flying usually have a pigeon house or loft which is divided into two compartments, one for breeding stock, the other for young unmated birds. In the latter there are no nest boxes but instead, either a series of individual perches dotted around the house or what looks like a bookshelf of "pigeon-holes" which allows birds to establish themselves in/on their own perch when at rest. For the beginner however, this division of young and old stock is seldom warranted, and small individual perches on the wall away from the nest box area should be adequate for youngsters who are growing up, getting through their first moult and developing into strong potential breeding stock.

These days the floor of the house or loft is usually covered in clean soft wood shavings which can be raked over daily, or more likely weekly, to keep it fresh, (the discarded portion being used on the compost heap to cover the weekly lawn mowings). Sand can be used in the same way, and in fact might be more appreciated by the birds but less by the gardener's compost (unless you are on a very heavy clay!). In either case it will be necessary to provide a heap of straw or fine twiggy material for nest building.

To complete the internal arrangements, food hoppers and drinkers will be needed, both of which should be a type which does not allow the birds to foul them (see diagram). A hopper for grit is also advisable, particularly where the birds are confined to aviary type housing.

Siting your pigeon house

Positioning of your polecote, wallcote or aviary is all important for the well being of your birds, as well as your own pleasure.

You should try to face your pigeon house south or south east. South east is best as the pigeons benefit from the warm early morning sun. Beware of placing a wallcote on certain south walls, which could become very hot in the summer. The site should offer some shade but should also be light and catch the sunshine so that the pigeons can synthesize vitamin D from the sun's rays.

Place your pigeon house in view of the kitchen, study or living room window, so that you can observe your birds. This is partly for therapeutic reasons, and partly so that if one of your birds finds itself in trouble you can be there quickly to sort it out; you will find too, that their behaviour and antics soon lead to them developing imaginary characteristics, often reminiscent of friends or relatives and other people you know!

The area should be dry so that the ground around is not muddy or soft, and be careful of prevailing winds so the pigeons are not draughty and can get away from bad weather.

It is most important that your polecote is firmly set in the ground. To achieve a good result use only wet mix concrete and hard core; do not use dry mix which is weak and useless. A proprietry fast-set mix is even better: Jewsons' Postfix sets very rapidly in one hour. You will probably need two 25kg bags at about £6 per bag. To hold the post vertically while the mix sets it is best to use two 8ft battens hammered into the ground at 45 degrees in different planes (N-S and E-W) and each attached to the main post by a nail. These will support it while the concrete sets.

Make sure your polecote is tall enough, 6' to 8' high, to stop cats from jumping up; also, that it is not placed too near fences or overhanging trees, to prevent cats and squirrels from jumping across to it. The same precautions should be taken against snakes, raccoons and possums for those people living abroad.

19

FOOD, DRINK, GRIT AND MINERALS

FOOD - When you see what pigeons will eat in the city parks, and then see what the expert pigeon keeper feeds his birds on, you wonder how they survive; a pigeon's diet is very varied.

In the racing and exhibition world, the pigeon fancier is fanatical about the rations he feeds to his birds, but as we are only keeping a few doves for our pleasure, there is no need to go into the intricacies of feeding hemp or lentils, etc. Needless to say, it is important to give your birds a balanced diet.

Most feed merchants stock pigeon food, and this contains maize, wheat, peas, beans and millet. Other seeds that can also be fed are barley, rolled oats, polished rice, lentils, vetches and canary seed. In addition to this a small quantity of poultry pellets (layers pellets) can be included. Wild bird food is a good standby if you are having trouble finding proper food.

The food must be kept dry and clean. The size of container you use depends upon the number of birds you have, but anything from a large tin with a lid to a plastic dustbin is ideal. The other important point is to keep rats and mice out.

The food should be hard and clean, i.e. the grains should be as hard as nails and not dusty. One wonders how the birds can digest these seeds, but having seen Woodpigeons with crops full of acorns, I know how good a digestive system a pigeon has. Some people say that you should not feed same season wheat, as they reckon it is not hard enough, but I think this depends on the season and the moisture content of the grain.

It is possible to mix your own feed starting with a basic 50% wheat and adding various grains; many people do this, but it is easier for the beginner to buy the ready mixed product. I know at the moment my pigeons will not touch beans or layers pellets, and too much of certain grains like maize can make your birds fat or give them diahorrea.

Buying from a feed merchant is cheaper than from a pet shop. You can find feed merchants in your local trade directories.

WATER - Clean drinking water is essential; some fanciers only give their birds bottled water. There are some infusions that can be added, such as garlic and herbs, and in fact there is a range of water soluble tonics and vitamins available, but most of these are for the serious pigeon breeder or racer.

TOP. A breeding nest box with hinged perch-cum-door open.
ABOVE. Breeding nest box with hinged perch-cum-door closed. Note the cardboard nesting bowl.

A nesting material box for use in an aviary.

A double nesting box. The floors pull out for cleaning. The centre partition is recessed to allow the pigeons to move from one side to the other.

Modena.

Black Nun.

Modenas. Large and handsome pigeons. There are two main types, Gazzi and Schietti and these come in many different colours.

A hawk strike in Stormy Gale's garden. Note the bird has been killed and eaten from the head down the neck and onto the back. A sparrowhawk was thought to be the culprit.

A young pigeon or squab just out of the nest and living on the floor, trying not to be picked on by adult birds. Note the long pink beak for reaching inside its parent's beak to feed.

Stormy Gale's Voorburg Shield Croppers. They were all a little spooked after the hawk raid.

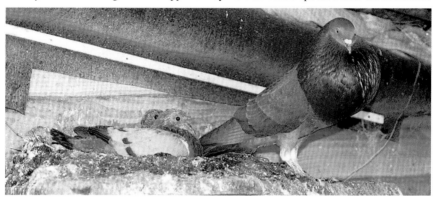

Horseman and squabs. You can see the mess squabs make in their nesting area, and it sets like concrete.

A pair of Horseman pigeons. They come in a range of different colours.

Horseman with chicks about 2-3 days old. At this stage they double their weight daily.

Different terra-cotta nesting
bowls lined with chopped straw.
The pigeons are West of England
Tumblers.

This picture shows clearly how doves and pigeons drink. They suck the water up in one
continuous draught.

Some of Veronica Mayhew's Voorbury Shield Croppers. They come in a range of different colours.

West of England Tumblers. These come in a variety of colours, and adapt well to polecotes or wallcotes.

West of England Tumbler.

This is an English long faced Tumbler.

A metal drinker. Note it is set up on two house bricks to stop any litter fouling the water.

GRIT - This is an important part of a pigeon's diet, as it is not only absorbed into the gut but also used in the gizzard for grinding down all the hard seeds that they eat. Poultry grit can be used, as this contains oyster shell, limestone and flint. Another useful grit is calcified seaweed which is rich in trace elements and salt; this is available at garden centres.

MINERALS AND VITAMINS - As we have seen elsewhere, salt is an important part of a pigeon's diet, but too much will kill them. Most breeders today buy mineral blocks or pots for their pigeons to give them the correct balance of minerals, vitamins and salt. These are quite inexpensive. If you keep sheep, you may find that your pigeons enjoy small quantities of the yellow sheep lick block. Charcoal is also fed in small amounts.

GREEN FEED - If your birds are confined to an aviary, a weekly feed of lettuce, chickweed or spinach is beneficial.

21

CONTAINERS - There are three golden rules for feeding pigeons: keep the food dry, that is away from the elements; keep the food hoppers up off the floor or on a shelf to stop floor litter or feathers from being flicked into them; and thirdly, keep the food covered, that is the hopper must have a steep sloping roof to stop the pigeons from perching on it and fouling the food - it must also have small apertures to allow the pigeon to get only his head and neck into the food to minimize the amount being chucked about. It is really best to buy a proper pigeon feeder made of plastic, ceramic or galvanized metal.

Some breeders prefer to feed their birds twice a day instead of ad lib feeding in hoppers, but this is a matter of choice.

CONTAINERS FOR WATER - This is very much the same story as for food hoppers. It is advisable to buy a proper pigeon drinker and the plastic ones are best, particularly if the weather is frosty. There are galvanized and earthenware drinkers as well. The drinker must be cleaned out and filled with fresh water every day. Stand it up off the floor so that dust, litter and feathers don't foul the water. There is a list of suppliers of drinkers and feeders etc. at the end of the book.

CONTAINERS FOR GRIT, MINERALS, VITAMINS AND GREEN FOOD - These should be in plastic or china, as the salt corrodes metal. There is a variety of cage cups, pots and hoppers for this purpose, and again, you should keep them off the floor to protect them from being fouled.

Plastic drinkers and feeder (centre).

OTHER REQUIREMENTS

Only two of these items, water ponds and nesting pans, are applicable to polecotes and wallcotes, the rest are for use in aviaries.

WATER POND This should be placed on the grass or the edge of the drive in view of the doves, or on the floor of the outside section of the aviary, so the pigeons can have a bath. Bathing is a very important activity for pigeons throughout the year. It helps to keep their feathers clean and in good order and also reduce any fleas and lice they may be carrying. The water in the bath should not exceed 3" (7.5cms) in depth so that young squabs do not drown if they get in. Fill the bath a couple of times a week, particularly on sunny days, and change the water daily while it is in use. There are galvanised metal or plastic baths available from your specialist pigeon suppliers, or you can buy a shallow container about 4" - 5" deep and 2' x 18" (10 - 12 cms deep and 60 x 46 cms) at your local garden centre. You can even buy pigeon bath salts to pamper your birds with! Incidently, bathing during the breeding season is said to help with the hatchability of the pigeons' eggs.

NESTING PANS These are mainly for use in nest boxes in aviaries, but can be used in polecotes and wallcotes. They are made of various materials such as cardboard or papièr-mâché which can be burned after use, or plastic and ceramic, both of which can be washed and reused. They help to make a nest where the eggs will not be scattered or rolled out.

White Garden Fantails feeding from a plastic pigeon feeder. The pointed lid kept blowing off, so I made two clips with elastic bands to hold it on.

PERCHES These come in many shapes and sizes to suit large or small aviaries. The perches for outside flight areas are mainly round or half round timber about 2½" wide, (6 cms). Inside, there can be inverted V perches, peg perches, box perches and 'L' shaped perches, and I have seen swinging perches in one aviary. The main consideration is ease of cleaning; also, never put any perches over feeding or drinking areas.

NEST BOXES These come in two forms, single nest boxes in the form of a box 12" x 12" (30 cms x 30 cms) or a line of such boxes, complete with landing platform and pop hole or entrance. The other type is a twin nest box, i.e. two nesting areas together, so the pigeons can nest continually. They can have one and a half nests on the go all the time during the breeding season! It is important that these boxes are made so that they are easy to clean, as after the squabs have left the nest, the area is in a dirty and verminous condition. False floors and/or nesting pans are a good idea, and it is also sensible to give the area a squirt with some anti-redmite spray.

NEST LITTER Part of a dove's courting ritual includes the presentation of nesting material by the cock to the hen, so nesting material needs to be on hand. Outside, with polecotes and wallcotes, it is easier as the doves will find twigs, stalks etc., but in an aviary a rack or container is necessary to hold straw, twigs, or even light prunings from the garden; this will keep the aviary tidy. Tobacco stalks can also be bought for nesting material and these help to deter lice and fleas.

The floor of the aviary Most people use shavings. The equine grade is best as it is less dusty. Other floor coverings can be sand or peat. I find that putting newspaper down first and shavings on top to a depth of 1½" (4 cms) is ideal.

Last but not least, hang up a Vapona strip in your aviary. This will help to kill any nasty insects inside the building. Remember, pigeons don't eat insects, they are grain eaters.

An inverted 'V' perch.

BREEDING

POLECOTES & WALLCOTES

There is no breeding control over your flock of pigeons in these two types of accommodation, except by the removal or pricking of eggs. Although the birds will generally mate for life, (providing one or the other does not die or get killed), your flock is open to strangers coming in. These are mainly feral or tired racing pigeons stopping on the way and not carrying on, (racing pigeons have a rubber ring on their leg as well as a closed ring - see ringing), so if you want to keep your flock pure, there may be a certain amount of culling to do, either by trapping them in their accommodation at night time, or with an air gun. A net can be thrown over the polecote, but this will not necessarily catch all the inmates.

Most people who keep pigeons under this system do not care too much about how their birds breed; they remove any eggs from mongrel pigeons and are happy as long as their birds are healthy and look good. It must be pointed out that in the south of England and warmer climates pigeons will breed all the year round except when they are moulting or shedding feathers, (August to October). So there can be quite a production line going, anything up to 10 clutches a year!

The birds will gather some of their own nesting material, straw, twigs, etc and more should be provided near the feeding area. Some nests will be very scant while other birds will gather piles of material. It is as well to clean these nests out every couple of months, as they harbour mites and fleas; I have even seen the odd maggot as well. Young pigeons or squabs are rather unhygienic. Most birds carry away their youngs' feaces, but squabs just go to the edge of the nest, lift their tails and let fly. Although pigeon manure is not particularly smelly, it does set very hard, and you will need a scraper blade to clean the nesting compartment. After cleaning give the area a good spray or sprinkle of Ban-Mite, Duramitex or Kill-Pest. Be sure to use a proprietary brand for use with pigeons, as they are very susceptible to chemicals.

If you can get to the young on the seventh day to ring them, (closed ring) so much the better, but it is not necessary with this method of keeping doves.

AVIARY

This is where you become aware of the intricacies of pigeon behaviour. Here you can choose which birds you want to breed from. This is not as simple as it may appear, because sexing birds, particularly young ones, can be difficult until after their first moult. Incidently, a certain amount of inbreeding is not as disastrous as some people think.

25

Various Wallcotes found on the market to-day, by courtesy of Forsham Cottage Arks, Kootensaw Dovecotes & WGF Dovecotes.

SELECTION

Obviously you want to keep the breed pure, but you are also breeding for type, colour, size and a number of other factors known only to you concerning the standard you are trying to maintain. Place the birds one in each half of a mating box or coop. This is a double box, 18" x 18" x 18" (46 x 46 x 46 cms) each side, with a removable wire partition down the middle. These boxes can vary in size depending on the breed. Both cages will require cage cups for feed and water, and some shavings or sand on the floor. After 3 - 5 days of looking at each other through the wire, the birds are placed together into a nesting box with a nest pan to settle down for a few days before being allowed access to the rest of the breeding area. Of course they are fed with cage cups while they are confined. Then comes the moment of truth: they are allowed out, but are they really a pair, or are they two females or two males? Obviously if there are no eggs, then they must be two cocks, and neither will sit on the nest at night. Conversely if there are four eggs, then you must have two hens, who will both sit on the nest at night, and the eggs are normally infertile, (although sometimes a wayward cockbird will fertilise one or both hens). So four eggs or no eggs at all, ring your birds and go back to the beginning. Curiously in these cases there are all the obvious signs of courtship and nest building so it is a great disappointment when this happens. Experience will help you, as each breed is different as well as each bird.

COURTSHIP

A male pigeon will spend hours, even days, courting or chatting up his loved one. This will involve pacing round in front of her, cooing away, his crop distended with air, lowering his head, fanning his tail and turning in circles. There is also a certain amount of fighting to push away other suitors. When the moment is right, and the female is sure about the male, she will advance towards him and start billing; this is a form of kissing. Later the male will feed her like a young squab, the female putting her beak down into his throat and taking regurgitated food. In due course she will crouch down and allow herself to be mated. This is known as the cloacal kiss, by which means the sperm is transferred to the female who then struts off as though very proud of herself. If the pair have free access, they will fly off with a loud clapping of wings.

NESTING

Towards the middle and end of the courtship period the male will seek out a nest box for his mate if one has not already been allocated, and he will fight valiantly for it. They will nest in the most precarious places and even on the floor, so it is important to have enough nest boxes to go round for the number of birds in the breeding area. Floor nesting should be discouraged for obvious reasons. Once the nest box is established, then you will often see the two birds sitting very tightly together inside, as if they are planning the decoration of their home! They will start to bring nesting material to the box and this can be provided in a container; it is normally a combination of straw, birch twigs, pine needles and tobacco stalks. Tobacco stalks and pine needles help to repel lice and fleas.

Most breeders use nesting pans; these are made of plastic, china or cardboard and can be washed or burned after each brood. Put some shavings and flea powder into the bowl to help keep the nest free of insects. At this stage the cock bird becomes more attentive to the hen bird, almost smothering her as if he is unsure of their bonding. This is called 'driving' and lasts until the first egg is laid. He will follow her everywhere and will even attack her if she does not conform to his wishes and become attached to the chosen nest site. One word of warning, when transporting a pair in this condition, always separate the two birds during the journey, as males have been known to kill their partners in their agitated state.

A Horseman pigeon sitting on a nest. Note the amount of twigs and straw this pair have needed to make a nest.

EGGS

When the nest is completed, the first egg will be laid and the second after 24 hours. The eggs are white, about 3.5 to 4 cm long and 2.5 to 3cm wide. Incubation starts after the arrival of the second egg. Pigeons have been known to lay three eggs but this is rare; also, watch out for the odd double-yolker as these are normally infertile and should be removed. One of the important reasons for using a bowl for the nest is to keep the eggs together. If one egg gets accidently rolled away on a flat nest the pigeon will very often sit on one egg and not have the sense to roll the other back under her, leaving it to cool on the side of the nest.

Freshly laid pigeon eggs are translucent and transmit light like pearls. As the eggs are brooded they will gradually turn opaque then develope a blue tinge. When they are hatching tiny chips will appear as the chick breaks out; don't feel tempted to "help" it as it is probably still attached to the membrane and blood vessels in the shell.

If you have too many pigeons breeding too fast you can remove the eggs but the birds will just lay more. Take the eggs out and prick them with a pin or needle then return them to the nest. The pigeons will continue to sit but the eggs will not hatch and the pigeons will not lay again for several weeks. Alternatively you can provide plastic, wooden or crock eggs for your birds to sit on.

INCUBATION

Incubation is shared by both birds and lasts for 17-18 days, depending on the climate and the time of year. The male sits on the eggs during the day from approximately 10 am to 4 pm, and the female has the longer night shift from about 4pm to the following morning. During the last few days of incubation, the female takes over full time and hatches the young. A sure sign that the eggs are fertile is that towards the end of the incubation period, they change colour and take on a bluish grey hue. You will see that even during incubation the male will bring nesting material, just to please his mate.

HATCHING

The squabs will take 24 hours to hatch, normally starting in the morning and hatching the following morning. Prior to hatching it is important for the parent birds to have access to bathing water, so that their moist under-feathers will help to soften the membrane within the eggshell. The chick, unusually, has two egg teeth and opens the egg in the neat, sawn around fashion of a chick with only one egg tooth; the purpose of the second tooth is unknown. The egg shells are removed by the parent birds who take it in turns to brood the young continuously. If there are any deformed or sickly squabs, now is the time to get rid of them.

SQUABS (sometimes called squeakers)

Squabs are born naked with their eyes shut; they are pink and look rather ugly. They have over-sized beaks for their heads and it is not until adulthood that they begin to fine down and look attractive. The beaks are soft and spadelike so that they can receive the semi-liquid, regurgitated, whitish substance often called pigeon milk from their parents. They are fed by both birds to begin with and later more by the male as the female attends to her new nest. As the squabs become older and more demanding, so the food becomes more solid, containing small grains and seeds, until the young birds can accept whole grains. After 5 days the eyes open and on the seventh day the quills start to appear giving the

A squab about 7 days old. Note the bulbous beak, the rather sleepy eyes, and the ear hole under and behind the eye.

squab a yellowish covering of down. It is on the seventh day that the closed ring is put on (see ringing). If a young squab drops out of the nest during rearing, it is sometimes abandoned, and there are cases of poor doers, where one squab will get the bulk of the food and the other will wither away. The parent birds will cover the squabs until they become fully feathered which takes 4 weeks from the time of hatching.

As the squabs grow, so does their appetite, and as soon as the parent arrives at the nesting box, there is much flapping of wings and loud squeaking, and the nesting area will gradually become more and more dirty.

30

LEAVING THE NEST

If the parents are doing the squabs well, the young will be reluctant to leave the nest, whereas squabs which are hard done by will be the earliest to leave. It is at this point that the squab is taken for eating as the breast muscle meat is at its best because the bird has not yet used it for flying. As the squabs' demand for food becomes greater, so the male bird slackens off the feeding and the young birds follow him out, fluttering to the floor. The male will generally carry on feeding them down there, and it is important at this stage to put feeders and drinkers on the ground, if you haven't already done so, in order that the young birds can find them. The young learn to feed themselves and to fly at the same time. (Some breeders who are using aviaries like to put a low shelf about 9" wide, and 6" off the floor, for the young squabs to hide under, as sometimes they can be attacked by adult birds. Once they are flying around, they can be removed to the young pigeon section, so they don't upset the birds in the breeding area). One tip on feeding young birds that have just started to take whole grains: keep the food small and avoid large pigeon beans as the young birds might choke.

BREEDING AGE

Pigeons will breed on average up to 8-10 years old and live for as long as 15 years or more.

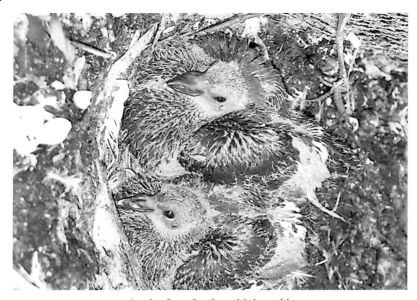

A pair of squabs about 16 days old.

31

BARREN HENS - There may be one or more reasons for this. Diet plays a large part, age, too much inbreeding and/or an accident perhaps. Often the hen bird will go through the nest building routines but will produce no eggs. If she is given some fertile eggs, she will hatch them and rear the squabs and this will generally break her barren habit, meaning that afterwards she should revert to a normal breeding cycle.

FOSTER PARENTS - We mention this although it is not really a beginner's problem. Certain of the fancy pigeons and doves, the short faced breeds such as Toys and Owls, have very short beaks and are therefore unable to feed their young, so the eggs are put under foster parents, normally Tumblers or Homers. Care should be taken to get the timing of the transfer right, so that foster parents are laying at approximately the same time as the donors. It is also possible to put squabs up to 7 days old under the foster parents. But you can see from this, that when breeding these particular kinds of pigeon you also have to breed foster parents for their propagation.

MOULTING - Pigeons don't moult like poultry, who sometimes lose all their feathers overnight. Moulting in pigeons is a gradual process, taking place normally in summer and autumn, but they do start to moult once they begin breeding and this can be as early as January.

This is Raj, our Indian Fantail.

SEXING

Aristotle (448 - 380 BC) wrote in his History of Animals: "pigeons usually produce one male and one female and of these the male is often hatched first". Oh, that it were that simple! Even Darwin went along with this theory, until the Victorian Harrison Weir reported that there were often two females in the same nest.

A French professor by the name of Monsieur Guenot, went further, and under laboratory conditions discovered that out of 65 nests, 17 nests had two males, 14 nests had two females and 34 nests had both sexes. He went on to investigate the theory that the first egg hatched was male. Again under laboratory conditions, out of 30 nests, the first egg hatched in 15 nests was male, and in the other 15 nests it was female, so there is no truth in this theory. However there is another theory that if both birds are weighed when the squabs are ready to leave the nest, the heavier one tends to be the cock bird.

So where does this lead? Pigeons are notoriously difficult to sex without careful observation of their habits. Let us put aside the possibility of same sex relationships as mentioned in Selection, and look for the signs that differentiate the sexes.

The male is slightly larger than the female, with a shorter and bolder head. The bill of the female looks longer because of the more slender head and neck. The male has a slightly thicker neck, coos more loudly and longer than the females and is more showy, particularly during courtship when he will turn round or pivot through 360° in front of her. It is the female who will take the regurgitated food during courtship, but the male who will bring the twigs or nesting materials to the nest for the female to arrange. When the female is laying, the pelvic bones have a wider gap between them to allow the passage of the eggs, and it is the female that sits on the eggs at night time. Pairs normally perch together when roosting at night, so that pairs of birds can be caught then if necessary. After a while you get an eye for sexing, but some birds can still fool you.

White Garden Fantail breeder Dave Brown of Fairlight in Sussex sexes his birds just prior to despatch when they are fully fledged and ready to fly. He uses the pelvic gap method, holding the young bird in his left hand facing right and feeling the pelvic structure with the second finger of his right hand. If the bones are close together the bird is male, if there is a wider gap and the finger can easily fit between them the bird is female. He then attaches a colour-coded ring (red or blue for males, green or white for females) which also carries a contact telephone number for his retrieval system.

Like poultry, pigeons can be colour sexed. This is called sex linking, and it involves mating one colour of pigeon to another, to produce male offspring of one colour and female of another, but most people breeding pigeons in the garden want to retain a single or certain colours, so this does not apply. There are also auto-sexed breeds. These are mainly found in the heavier breeds such as Kings, Carneau etc. which naturally throw one colour or colour pattern for the males and another for the females. This is really for the commercial pigeon keepers, so that they can tell when the squabs are feathered what to breed from or what to kill.

Having talked about the difficulty in sexing pigeons, I would like to mention an old Arab method. (I have not tried it myself so I can't vouch for how successful it is). The pigeon is held in the palm of one hand standing up with its legs held between the thumb and index finger. With the thumb and index finger of the other hand, you point the pigeon's beak towards the sun and gently rock the bird forwards. The tail of the unbalanced pigeon fans out and goes either up or down. If it goes up the bird is female and if it goes down it is male!

WHAT DO I DO WHEN THE PIGEONS FIRST ARRIVE?

POLECOTES & WALLCOTES

With these in place, you will need to keep your newly arrived birds confined inside so that they will adjust their homing instincts to their new location. They should be confined for 4 weeks, but it must be said that some breeds of pigeon have stronger homing instincts than others, so it is always best to ring or mark your birds as soon as they arrive, (see Handling and Ringing) so that if they do fly back home when released, you can recognise them. Garden Fantails seem to be quite good at settling down in their new location, but with some breeds like Homers you will need to buy unflighted birds, ie feathered squabs who have not yet developed a strong homing instinct.

A polecote with netted frame, during the confinement of the doves. The narrow door at the back is access for feeding and watering.

POLECOTE

There are various ways of confining doves in a polecote. One method is to make a net tent enveloping either all or a portion of the polecote so that the pigeons can have access to the ground, and also have enough room to flutter upwards to the polecote, and get away from cats and dogs. Another method is to make a box similar to the one used for the wallcote, (see below), and use that for confinement, and you must make provision to feed and water your birds safely. The box system seems to work best, particularly if you have other birds using the polecote, although your birds can't fly during confinement. The netting method requires fruit cage netting and several lengths of timber lath or tile battens.

WALLCOTE

A box should be constructed to fix to the front of the wallcote; it should have a wire mesh front and floor, and plyboard top and sides so that the birds have some protection from the elements, while being able to see out and get their bearings. A small door on the front or side serves to put the birds in and to feed and water them. Feeding and watering must be a daily exercise as when the birds are confined like this, the food and water can easily become contaminated; you will also find that the area under the wallcote becomes rather messy. (This does not happen normally as the birds are out and about on the drive, lawn, roof etc).

A temporary "confining" box on a wallcote. The door was taken off after a month to allow the birds access to the outside world, and to stop it from flapping in the wind. The wire mesh floor helps to keep the box clean during confinement.

Feather stamping, with the owner's name and telephone number.

A pigeon house from Luxor, South Egypt.

Pigeon nesting boxes, made of mud and straw, as found in the Luxor area.

A large modern polecote from Kuig Dovecotes.

AVIARY (EMPTY)

The problem of confinement does not exist as the pigeons only have access to the aviary. If it is empty, then simply put your birds onto the floor where the food and water is. Leave them to be quiet for a hour or two, and sneak in to check that they are up on the perches. The male will probably start cooing and dancing around. Aviary (with birds already inside). If you are adding birds to your aviary, the best plan is to shut them into a nest box with a front on, and feed and water them for 3 to 4 days in the nest box, so that the existing birds become acquainted with them, then open the door and let them out into the aviary. If you just put the new pair or pairs in willy-nilly, there will be quite a lot of fighting and your nice new birds could end up looking the worse for wear.

After 4 weeks open the small door and fasten it back to allow the birds in and out of the polecote or wallcote. It is best to do this on a still evening when there is no wind. This can be a nail biting time as your doves find their way out and take off. In general it works well; as often as not, they will go and sit on your neighbours' roof or T.V. aerial, but there are times when there is a bird with a particularly strong homing instinct and he or she will take the whole flock off back to their original home. After a week or two, the confinement box can be taken down, cleaned and stored away. You may need to feed your birds on the drive or lawn under the wallcote until they find your feeding station, if you have one.

New pigeons being added to a flock must still be confined for 4 weeks.

An outside veranda on a pigeon shed, so the birds have access to the sun.

RINGING AND HANDLING

The reason for ringing is identification.

A)   Ownership

B)   Year of birth

C)   Male or female

D)   Breeding line.

CLOSED RINGS

If your birds have access to free flight or you wish to show them then closed ringing is the norm. These rings are normally made of aluminium, and can come in seven different colours. You can have your name, address and telephone number printed on them, and a wide variety of information, but it is all governed by the space on the ring. These rings are put on the squab on day 7, much earlier and they can come off, much later and the ring will not fit over the toes and leg, and can cause damage to the scales on the leg. Unfortunately at this age you cannot tell the sex of the bird, but always ring the same side leg for each year. Thus with seven different colours it is possible to ring for 14 years without a problem. These rings can be purchased from your local club or from a pigeon accessory supplier. See the list at the back of the book.

SPIRAL (COIL) RINGS

These rings are made of plastic, normally in 15 different colours, and are also available with numbers. They are cheap and easy to put on: just uncoil the ring a little and roll it around the leg until it is on, taking care not to harm the scales on the pigeon's leg. From these rings you can tell at a glance without catching the bird whether it is male or female, what year it was hatched and from which bloodline, etc.

CLIP RINGS

These come in 15 different colours and are perhaps less fiddly than spiral rings. Place the ring around the leg and snap it shut, no special tool is required. If you want to change it just slide the ends in opposite directions to open.

RUBBER RACE RINGS

If you have a bird fly in, and it has an aluminium ring and a rubber ring on, then this is a racing pigeon which has stopped off or got lost. The rubber ring is placed on the leg by expanding it with a special four pronged tool. If the pigeon can be caught, then the Royal Pigeon Racing Association, The Reddings, Near Cheltenham, Glos GL51 6RN, telephone number 01452 713529, should be contacted. Don't forget to read the number on the aluminium ring.

Some people put innoculation rings on their birds stating: "I am innoculated against Paramyxo Virus". These birds should be disease free.

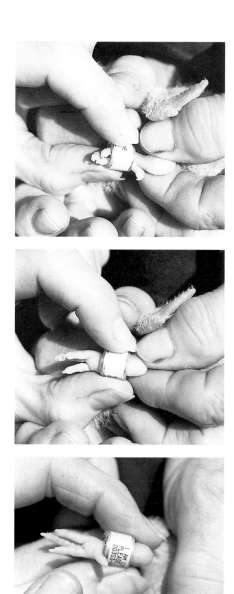

Putting a closed ring on a squab's leg at day seven. Thread the front three toes into the ring, slide the ring up the leg over the back toe, and then slide it back down, so that it is round the leg and cannot slide off because of the back toe.

OTHER METHODS OF MARKING OR IDENTIFICATION

Feather Stamping: This is often seen on racing pigeons. The flight feathers, the long end feathers on the wing, are marked with a rubber stamp with the name of the Club or breeder and the telephone number. This system only works on light coloured feathers.

Tattooing: This is mainly practiced by the exhibition pigeon people, as a positive method of identification. It is not often seen.

HANDLING

When catching a pigeon, do so quickly and firmly, without damaging or losing any feathers, and always with warm hands. Some pigeons are very tame, allowing themselves to be picked off the perch, others require a small landing net to catch them, if your aviary is large enough. These nets can be bought at the local fishing tackle shop; a short handled one is best, and you may need to modify it, otherwise you will find it will catch on anything protruding in the aviary. Catch the pigeon against the wire or on the floor, and hold it firmly in the net. Untangle it carefully, and hold it in the palm of one hand, your 3rd and 4th fingers holding the legs and the index finger and thumb holding the wing feathers. The pigeon feels comfortable in this position, and normally sits there enjoying the attention. To loose the pigeon, either just let it go into the air, or release it onto the floor gently.

If you don't want to disturb your pigeons unduly, catch them at night while they are on the perch. Pairs of pigeons normally roost together, making it easy to catch a pair.

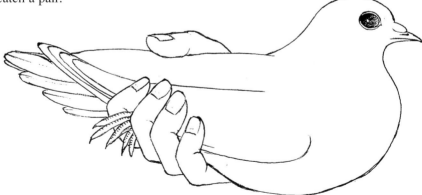

The correct way to hold a pigeon.

DISEASES & AILMENTS

We haven't gone very deeply into the subject of diseases and ailments, as this is covered in other publications and by more experienced people than ourselves. Suffice it to say that a little knowledge can be a dangerous thing and too much can be confusing. If your birds are dying it is best to have them post mortemed to find out what is going on and also which drug to use to clear up the problem. If you can catch a bird before it dies and take it to the vet, he or she has a better chance of diagnosing the problem, than with a bird that has already died. At the back of the book is a list of avian vets.

Prevention is everything. You are unlikely to have any problems if your birds are housed correctly in dry airy conditions with access to plenty of light and sunshine. There should be a regular cleaning programme, the food should be balanced, clean and dry, water should be changed daily and not placed in the direct rays of the sun, and there should be a correct supply of grit and minerals.

If you are buying in new stock, it is best to quarantine the new birds away from your resident ones, perhaps in your garage; don't forget to worm them as well. This also applies to exhibition stock, as diseases can abound at shows, (mainly caught from cages and drinking cups that have not been disinfected). Keep your exhibition stock apart from your other birds for 2 -3 weeks after the show and look out for any signs of colds, rattles, etc. Always feed and water the quarantine birds after having done your other birds, or get someone else to do it.

In an aviary set up, where birds are confined and more concentrated, be a little careful about visitors, particularly other pigeon breeders and dealers taking surplus stock, as there are some diseases that can be carried on clothing, hands and shoes. People with polecotes and wallcotes have few problems with this.

Here are some of the more common complaints found in pigeons, so that you can be aware of them.

External Parasites. Lice, fleas, red mite, feather mite. If you have a bird looking off colour, it might have a lice or flea burden. Lice live on the bird, fleas live on and off the bird, and red mite live mainly off the bird and are found as reddish grey clusters in the cracks of the nest boxes and round the perch area. All of these parasites feed on the bird in one way or another. They are normally introduced by wild birds, so there is no way of eliminating them altogether. If you keep your nest boxes well cleaned, sprayed and dusted and your pigeons have regular water baths, you should be able to keep these pests at bay. Ectofen is effective as a water based spray, or Johnson's Kil-pest powder can be used on the bird or in the nest box. Tobacco stalks can also be useful. If you put some down near their feeding place the pigeons will take them up to the dovecote and make a nest with them. When the bird sits on the nest the stalks warm up releasing fumes which deter feather lice. Tobacco stalks are available from most pigeon equipment suppliers.

Internal Parasites. Round, tape and hair worms. Again these are mainly spread by wild birds or introduced by new stock. There are several ways of purging your pigeons of worms: there are pills which are given to the bird individually and there are other wormers which are introduced in the water or the food. People with aviaries can choose their method, but those people with polecotes or wallcotes are best to medicate the feed. There are few signs of worms, until it is almost too late. The bird will look off colour, will not lay, will lose weight and the droppings will be runny. Garlic used to be the traditional and natural remedy for worms, but most people use Panacur, Piperazine, Avicas, and Harkers.

PARAMYXOVIRUS (PMV) This is a virus that is carried by collared doves and feral pigeons. It is highly contagious although not always fatal. It is important to realise that the disease can be excreted and spread for up to six weeks while the birds appear normal, and is shed in largest quantities towards the end of incubation and in the early stages of the disease with the birds still looking healthy. The first signs are very watery droppings and a prevailing unpleasant smell. The birds will start trembling and shivering, falling over and twisting their necks and limping. Their feathers can be affected and become wavy or twisted, sometimes developing white patches at the ends. Treatment is in the form of injection by the vet in the back of the neck. Young birds can be vaccinated once they are over three weeks old; large flocks can be treated with Hitchner Poulvac B1 Vaccine that is added to the drinking water. It is important to have your birds re-vaccinated periodically to keep up their immunity. Please note: it is a legal requirement that all birds must be vaccinated prior to showing or racing.

CANKER This is caused by a protozoa Trichomonas gallinae or columbae and is spread from bird to bird by feeding, billing and drinking out of the same water container; it can also be found in damp or wet areas of your aviary. The birds show few symptoms except for a small infection at the corner of the beak but in squabs it is more visible as a yellow cheesy matter inside the mouth and throat. This can eventually spread across the back of the mouth restricting the food intake and breathing. This disease affects the liver and digestion. Most pigeon breeders have an anti-canker treatment programme before and after the breeding season. There are various medications for this including Harkanker and Spartrix.

COLDS, RATTLES, SNEEZES In loose terms, infections of the lungs, bronchials, windpipe and nasal cavities. There are many diseases which occur in these areas, giving rise to sneezes, watery eyes, smelly nasal discharges, rattles in the throat and birds looking thoroughly off colour with their feathers all fluffed up as if they are cold. This is mainly seen in aviary birds and not so much in birds living in polecotes or wallcotes. There is a problem here as some of these colds and rattles are resistant to certain drugs, so it is no good going to your vet and asking for Terramycin and then finding that the disease is resistant to it. It is best to take a sick bird to your vet for swabbing, and then the right antibiotic can be identified and used. Suitable drugs are Terramycin, Aureomycin or Tylan, etc.

COCCIDIOSIS (commonly called Coxy). This is a protozoan parasite of which there are many. It always seems to appear when the weather is damp, or perhaps when the litter becomes wet in the aviary; it is also very much a stress related disease. Symptoms include discoloured and watery diahorrea and birds looking cold and mopey. Most of the treatments for Coxy are introduced into the drinking water. There are several appropriate manufacturers about including Harkers, Norvet and Vanhee.

I designed this polecote so that the accommodation is lowered down for cleaning and inspection. The central panel hinges open in order to be able to clean the nest boxes properly. This polecote is six sided, the same as a honeycomb, and can house 18 pairs of doves.

NAILS AND BEAKS There are times, particularly with older birds, when their toenails and beaks will require trimming. (It is important to keep their beaks in good shape so that the pigeons can continue to feed properly). This should be done with proper nail cutters and cutting should be at an angle to the nail or beak, not across it. Only take a little off at a time and be careful of the blood vessel in both beak and nails.

Just a word of warning about using drugs on pigeons: there are certain poultry drugs that will kill pigeons, so always use medications and disinfectants which are known to be safe with them.

PIGEONS AND THE GARDEN

Since this is about the pleasure of keeping pigeons, perhaps a few remarks about their relationship with that other popular source of enjoyment, namely gardening, might be warranted. A quality dovecote in a practical design and correctly positioned, (ideally where you can see it from your sitting room or conservatory), will undoubtedly enhance the value of your property.

As already stated, a dovecote on a pole certainly does something for a garden. Perhaps it adds the final touch to the sought after sense of peace and tranquillity, or perhaps the pigeons themselves add to the natural colours, sounds and movements one likes to imagine in an ideal garden. In the latter case the type of house is not of major importance and the garden shed type may be screened by a trellis so that only the roof is visible (with the pigeons on it of course!) whereas the aviary, in which one wants to be able to see the birds, would be more fully exposed, with shrubs or creepers covering only the windward side. For this purpose, light rather than heavy plant cover will be wanted, and therefore any of the Clematis montana group should be avoided as they will smother the whole structure in less than no time unless constantly cut back, in which case they will seldom flower, their main asset. Similar remarks could be made about Honeysuckle (Lonicera); although slower growing they can become equally dense. However, amongst both the Clematis and Honeysuckle families there are some less vigorous but equally attractive varieties which might be worth considering, for instance any Clematis which are cut right back each year before flowering, usually the early, large flowered types. With Honeysuckle, the shrubby varieties such as Hack's Red (L. tatarica), rather than the climbers should be preferred.

Annuals mainly of the Convolvulus group, or Morning Glory (an Ipomea) will quickly scramble up the wire netting, flower profusely through the summer and leave sufficient, though dead, cover to provide some protection from the winter winds. However they will need to be replanted each year. The same applies to Black-Eyed Susan. Others worth looking at are Passion flowers and the brilliant red Tropaclum tuberoeum (flowers like nasturtiums) which usually seeds itself and/or with luck forms its own tubers from which it resprouts each year.

Roses too could be very useful for this purpose as the routine annual pruning they need should ensure that they do not get out of control. Albertine, one of the oldest favourites of the climbers, with an abundance of scented salmon pink flowers seems to grow almost anywhere, and New Dawn, pale pink, also fragrant, has the advantage that it will tolerate a north facing site.

Shrubs worth trying as screens could include Cotoneaster horizontalis which will grow flat against the side of the aviary or house, with dark red autumn foliage and bright red berries into the winter, or Winter jasmin (Jasminum midiflorium) with yellow sprays of flowers from November right into the spring.

What plants would pigeons eat and/or damage in a garden? The only ornamental plant that I have ever seen pigeons show any interest in is Stonecrop (Sedum). This succulent evergreen seems to attract their attention at certain times of the year, whether as food or, like the black-birds, for the grubs to be found in or under the clumps, or for both, is not clear, but since stonecrop can become a pernicious weed in gravel paths and in garden beds it is unlikely that anyone will begrudge the pigeons whatever they get out of it.

As regards the vegetable garden, domestic pigeons do not seem to have the same passionate liking for Brassicas (the cabbage family) as do the wild Woodpigeons which can defoliate a crop over-night. In fact well fed domestic pigeons will pay little attention to the vegetable plot; they prefer to roam over the lawn picking out the young grass shoots, leaves and seeds of white clover and the seeds of other common weeds found in the less than perfect lawns such as mine! It is possible that hungry pigeons might behave differently, but if they are fed regularly there should be no adverse effects from keeping pigeons in your garden.

How can pigeon manure be used in the garden? For centuries the droppings which accumulated in the bottom of the large pigeon houses in the Middle East and Mediterranean countries, (described elsewhere), have been spread on the land. In the relatively hot dry climate of that area the breakdown into a product that was easy to handle would have been more rapid than might be expected in the more humid cooler atmosphere of this country. It would therefore not be suitable to recommend the use of pigeon manure on its own direct on to the garden by pigeon keepers over here. However, if you clean out the droppings daily or weekly and add them to your compost heap, the manure will help activate the compost and improve the structure or openness, as well as adding to the organic value of the final product. For those others who are less enthusiastic about cleaning out and who might leave the job for a major operation once a year, there may be a few difficulties. Problems may arise because the moist droppings will pack down tightly, and because air is excluded, anaerobic instead of aerobic decomposition will result in noxious odours when the manure is eventually dug out. This will occur to a lesser extent if wood shavings or straw are regularly put down as in the case of a deep litter poultry house. However, with hens scratching and constantly turning it over the litter is always well aerated, anaerobic conditions are avoided and so are undesirable smells. Unfortunately pigeons are not so obliging and the litter will either have to be turned regularly or when eventually dug out, stacked and allowed to rot down for some time until decomposed sufficiently to be useful in the garden.

A fine example of a round dovecote at Antony (NT), just over the Tamar from Plymouth, built in the 18th Century.

Inside the Antony dovecote, complete with revolving collecting frame.

PIGEON PREDATORS

Pigeons face two main kinds of predation, one from the air and the other from the ground.

The main threat from the air comes from peregrine falcons, goshawks, sparrowhawks, buzzards, and the odd female kestrel. There is not much one can do about this as all these birds are protected in the UK. It is time that the peregrine falcon was controlled in certain areas as their numbers have increased and they are no longer the rare bird that they were so many years ago. Goshawks are indiscriminate killers; their reintroduction to this country was the most senseless idea as experience from abroad, especially Australia, shows that in certain areas people dare not let their pigeons out at all. Of course the siting of your wallcote or polecote is all important, so that you can keep an eye on your birds from the kitchen or sitting room window. If there is a strike from a hawk, you may see it, and get out in time to save your bird, or at least relieve the hawk of its meal, thus deterring it from coming back. Also, activity such as children playing, dogs or cats running about, or gardening going on in the vicinity of your birds will help to deter any raider. I have a suspicion that tawny owls could also be a problem as I know they will attack pheasant poults.

Hovering birds of pray can be deterred in country areas with small rockets fired from a piece of metal tubing stuck in soft earth by a house door, and aimed 10ft to 20ft in front of the hovering pest.

If you are having serious problems with hawks there is a product available for putting coloured transfers in a bullseye design onto the wings of light coloured birds. This does not hurt or impede the pigeons, but these "terror eyes" are said to put off would-be predators, in the same way that some butterflies have "eyes" marked on their wings. This company also markets "Terror eye" balloons which have a similar effect and can be placed around dovecotes and aviaries. For details see the back of the book.

Crows and magpies when feeding young will enter dovecotes and take eggs or young squabs.

The main predator on the ground is the cat. Most breeds of pigeon suitable for wallcotes and polecotes would be able to cope, but the problem lies with squabs learning to fly and also the heavier breeds of pigeon. This is why the heavier breeds are kept in aviaries, where they are happy and have no fears. Cats can be caught in wire mesh live catch traps, and if feral can be taken to the relevant authorities, and there are several methods available for harmlessly deterring cats with sprays and water jets. A super-soaker type water gun is best, with ice-cold water!

Rats and mice can be a problem in the aviary. This is because food left scattered around will attract them in winter; so keeping the aviary clean and putting food in proper containers which are removed at night should deter rats and mice from wanting to come in. Rats will kill pigeons, particularly squabs, eating all the flesh and leaving only the legs, feet, wings and bones. Both rats and mice are carriers of diseases, not only through their droppings but also their urine which you can't see. Details about controlling rats and mice are to be found in "Modern Vermin Control", also from the Gold Cockerel series of books.

Pigeons are sensitive and fearful creatures as they are prey birds. They will not leave the aviary or polecote if there is a hawk about, and will fly and alight in flocks so as to reduce the possibility of being attacked. They do not like change, or loud and sudden noises like gunshots, and are particularly nervous at night.

On a different tack, I saw an article in a magazine which showed a pigeon with a series of loops of wire attached to a saddle on its back. This live pigeon decoy is used for trapping hawks. The hawk stoops onto the pigeon, its long toes become entangled in the loops, and thus the falconer is able to capture the bird. This is standard practice around the Middle East.

The monument to the Cathars at Minerve, France, showing a dove of peace cut through a slab of rock.

RACING PIGEONS

There should be a mention of racing pigeons in this book, in case you get the pigeon-bug and might be tempted to get involved with this fascinating world.

Most people associate racing pigeons with miners but in fact these birds attract people from many walks of life - the Royal family has a loft of racing pigeons for instance.

Originally (racing) pigeons were used to carry important messages. This goes back thousands of years, to times of war and siege and even the Olympic games in ancient Greece. More recently they were again used in times of war and also for conveying news of a financial and administrative nature, but have since been overtaken by radio, telegraph and telecommunications. France still retains a military Transmission regiment with 150 pigeons in its lofts.

There are four very interesting points about racing pigeons: first, the long and detailed pedigrees that they have, something akin to racehorses; second, the great speed at which they travel, between 60-70 mph, (for instance, a bird returning from Rennes in Northern France gets home to Cirencester, Gloucestershire in about 3 hours, a distance of 224 miles!); third, the racing pigeon world has its classic races such as the Barcelona and the Bordeaux just as the horse racing world has its Derby or Grand National. (The prize money is not the same but the value of the bird or its blood line is greatly enhanced by a win); fourth, the prices paid for these birds can be enormous: £100,000 for a pigeon is quite common and prices like these have made several people millionaires in Britain.

There are racing pigeon shows the length and breadth of the country, the largest of which is called The Best Homing Show of the Year and is held at Blackpool during the third week in January. Details about this and other shows are available from The Royal Pigeon Racing Association, see names and addresses at the back of the book.

This Middle Egyptian glyph is one of the first known showing pigeons carring messages. The messages may possibly warn of the forthcoming annual inundation of the Nile travelling northwards.

49

SHOWING PIGEONS

There are scores of pigeon shows around Britain organised by the National Pigeon Association. (NPA). The mouthpiece for this organisation is the magazine Feathered World, (see address at the back). Apart from interesting articles about pigeon keeping from this country and abroad, it is also a very good source for buying breeds of pigeons and doves.

If you are taken by a particular breed, then it is always best to visit the breeder, particularly if it is an exhibition breed. He will give you masses of information about those birds, their management, breeding, feeding and showing, far more than you would ever find in a book.

Showing is an art and a science, it is knowing when to start to breed, what birds to breed with, and a host of other factors in order to have your birds at their best for a particular date.

To try to cover the whole subject of showing in sufficient detail in just a few paragraphs would be impossible, but it can be one of the most rewarding pastimes. It doesn't necessarily involve a great deal of work, but is more a matter of having a good eye for detail. If you want to show your birds, go and learn from a showman or breeder, and you will make many friends if you join a pigeon club and do some showing.

A basket for carrying show birds, with four seperate compartments

50

THE ORIGIN OF THE DOMESTIC PIGEON

First of all there is the question, "what is the difference between a pigeon and a dove?" The same question may be asked about the difference between a horse and a pony. Structurally there is no difference between pigeons and doves, but in general, if a pigeon is small, dainty and attractive it is normally referred to as a dove. There are also differences in the shape of the head.

I am not aware of any D.N.A. studies of domestic pigeons and their progenitors, although I am sure they must have been investigated, possibly by the Germans or the Dutch; however, it is fairly conclusive that the domestic pigeon originated from the Rock dove with some assistance from the Stock dove. What is amazing is the diversity of domestic breeds: there are more than 400 that have been created by man.

The head of a Dodo, a member of the pigeon family

In the wild the pigeon family extends to over 450 species, from Sand grouse to Diamond doves to the extinct Dodo. Most of them have three common traits: A) the way they drink water, B) a connection with salt and C) the way they feed their young. A) they don't sip water, i.e. they don't raise their heads between each drink but take continuous draughts of water which would seem to confirm the theory that they probably originated from arid areas; (if you live in an arid region it is important to be able to quickly take in as much water as possible in one go), hence the link with Sand grouse. B) Salt. Rock doves are nearly always to be found on cliffs near the sea and here is a connection between salt and pigeons. Mr. Gale tells us that when he releases his birds from their house, they make straight for a salt mineral block in the next field, placed there for sheep.

Pliny, the Roman writer mentions: "for chicks at first they collect a saltish earth in their throat and disgorge it into their beaks, to get them in proper condition for food". Every pigeon keeper knows the importance of salt and minerals for his birds; recently I saw feral pigeons at Dawlish in Devon eating seaweed on the beach, and very smart they looked too, unlike the scruffy pigeons one sees in the city centres. C) The unique method of feeding their young with 'milk'. This is a cheesy substance formed by the cells of the lining epithelium of the crop, the walls of which undergo a marked thickening during the incubation period, while at the same time increasing in high fat content.

I mentioned the Stock dove (Columba oenas translated as Dove one) which is closely related to the Rock dove (Columba livia translated as Dove, livid or black and blue). The Stock dove is slightly larger than the Rock dove, with less barring on the wings and a blue rump instead of a white one. The name Stock comes from old Saxon meaning stump or stick, but unlike the Rock dove that never perches on trees, only on rocks, the Stock dove is at home in trees as well as rocks. Incidentally, the Woodpigeon played no part in the domestication of pigeons, being entirely a tree dweller. The Stock dove, or Blue rock as he is commonly called in the country, will nest in hollows in trees, fissures in rocks, church towers and old buildings, and is also known to use old rabbit burrows. This leads on to another interesting point about pigeons. They lay white eggs. Most birds that lay white eggs, owls, woodpeckers, sand martins or kingfishers for instance, lay them in holes in trees or holes in the ground, the egg being white so that they can see them more easily in the gloom. The eggs are not camouflaged like pheasants', plovers' or seagulls' eggs. This is particularly curious as the Stock dove's relation, the Woodpigeon, makes a very flimsy platform nest of twigs and lays two white eggs which can be clearly seen; no camouflage has developed over the years to protect them, but this could be because of the male/female incubation process which ensures that the nest is never left unattended. Incidently the Sand grouse lays a purpley-brown blotched egg on a sandy yellow background, good camouflage for the desert.

One of the West Country's oldest dovecotes built of stone, at Pridhamsleigh near Buckfastleigh. (Circa 13th century).

PRIDHAMSLEIGH DOVECOTE

LISTED IN 16TH. CENTURY RECORDS OF
9TH. CENTURY MANOR OF PRIDHAMSLEIGH
RESTORED IN 1976–7 BY ASHBURTON
AND TOTNES AMENITY SOCIETIES
FOR ADMISSION APPLY TO FARM OPPOSITE

A road sign on the N20 in France, indicating the regional interest in pigeon houses.

This eight pillared dovecote on the side of the road (N20) has been recently relocated and restored. In the central south of France, the number and different types of dovecotes are staggering.

A hawk has been shot and hung up to deter other hawks.

Pigeon houses in the Fayoum area. They stand about 20 to 30 ft high, are built of mud and chopped straw, and look rather bizarre. The houses hold hundreds of nesting pairs of pigeons.

Breeding boxes made of split bamboo cane, near Cairo, Egypt. Note the double nest boxes.

Squabs for sale in a market in Cairo. The birds can't fly, so they cling onto the straw for safety.

Another Fayoum type pigeon house. They are rather like giant seaside sandcastles, and inside the walls are lined with clay nesting jars.

Inside a northern Nile delta pigeon tower showing the construction. The wooden beams are used during construction, as perches for the pigeons, and as access to the nests when the tower is inhabited.

A clay or terra-cotta jar used as a pigeon nest box.

A close-up of the construction inside, showing the dark nesting jars and the light access pipes.

A pigeon tower nearing completion, with the top narrowing inwards, prior to roofing.

A small tower nearing completion, no roof yet. The walls are rendered smooth and painted white.

This DIY pigeon house, on the roof of a cottage is there to attract pigeons. There are many like this to be seen on the roofs of small houses in the Nile delta.

This pigeon house is to be found in the grounds of a famous hotel in the Fayoum area, but it is not typical of that district.

Commercial pigeon towers capable of housing thousands of pigeons. Note the different styles and entrance hole patterns.

An Egyptian farm yard with two small pigeon towers. There are crates nearby for taking the squabs to market.

Details of a pigeon tower, showing the straw/mud construction.

An unusual pigeon house, with two towers sharing the same base.

This pigeon house in the northern delta region, is slightly different with a large opening under a canopy on the top. Note the anti-rat shelf running round the entire house.

MAN'S ASSOCIATION WITH PIGEONS

Most people think of man's earliest association with pigeons or doves as being Noah releasing a dove from the ark (Genesis chapter 8). On the second release after a period of seven days 'the dove came in to him in the evening, and lo, in her mouth was an olive leaf pluckt off .'

A mosaic on the floor of the abbey in Caunes-Minervois, depicting a dove and an olive branch

What is clear from early archeological finds, is that primitive man living and sheltering in caves ate pigeon meat, whose bones were similar to Rock doves. This is not surprising as Rock doves live and nest in cliffs where such caves are found, and early man must have gathered squabs from these nests.

As man evolved from being a hunter-gatherer to cultivating crops, the pigeon was never far away. In fact the dovecote pigeon has always been a semi-feral bird, and as man developed he found that by constructing places (nest boxes) on his house or storage barns, he was able to entice the pigeons to leave their cliffs and use these constructions, which they did because food was nearby.

It is from the Bible again that we get our first suggestion of doves or pigeons becoming semi-domesticated and beginning to live with man, which we see in the book of Isaiah chapter 60: 'who are these that fly as a cloud and as the doves to their windows?'

We know from archeological finds that the first domestication took place in the Middle East, in the area of Mesopotamia (Iraq) and Persia (Iran). As civilization moved north, west and south from this area, so the habit of pigeon keeping continued, evolved and was refined. Purpose built constructions with nest boxes and perches were made to attract pigeons; their meat became a source of protein, and recognised breeds began to appear. In this way it developed into a farming practice which was mainly controlled by the rich and powerful of the land.

One of the earliest records of pigeon keeping comes from Egypt. There are records of pigeon, probably Turtle dove, being eaten, that go back as far as 3,000 BC, but early evidence of keeping pigeons in pigeon houses comes in the form of a decorative vase from the Theban tomb of Sebekhotpe, date 1420 - 1411 BC, showing a pigeon on its house.

This painting on the tomb of Sebekhotpe at Thebes (date 1420-1411) is probably the first showing a pigeon on a pigeon house.

A bas-relief, (engraved stone), from the temple in Dendera, Egypt, clearly shows two pigeons with packages attached to their necks. Pigeons were not only used to carry messages, but were also kept for their meat. In one bas-relief dating from 2,500 BC, pigeons can be seen being force-fed. The ancient Egyptians were clever at netting various birds including quail, ducks, geese and pigeons and this can again be seen in many bas-reliefs. When the birds were netted many were kept in aviaries as a means of storing food. Most pigeons depicted in bas-reliefs are Turtle doves, but some are Rock doves from which our domestic pigeon originally developed.

From the Middle East pigeon culture spread north west to Turkey and Greece. The Greeks used pigeons to carry the news of their Olympic games to the parts of Greece which had sent competitors. The Romans brought pigeon keeping into Italy and western Europe, and it also spread along the coast of north Africa to Morocco and north through Spain and Portugal. The south of France, in the area of Carcassonne, was the Romans' great grain growing region and it was from here that pigeon culture travelled north to England. The Roman writer Pliny noted at that time:

"Moreover also they (pigeons) have acted as go-betweens in important affairs, when at the siege of Modena Decimus (44-43 BC) Brutus sent to the consuls' camp despatches tied to their feet; what use to Antony were his rampant and watchful beseiging force, and even the barriers of nets that he stretched in the river, when the message went by air? Also pigeon fancying is carried to insane lengths by some people: they build towers on their roofs for these birds, and tell stories of the high breeding and pedigrees of particular breeds, for which there is now an old precedent: before Pompey's civil war (49 BC) Lucius/Axius, Knight of Rome, advertised pigeons for sale at 400 denarii per brace!" (One denarius was a silver coin worth about a man's daily pay which in today's terms means £50, so that a brace of pigeons was offered for £2,000.)

Although the Romans probably introduced pigeon keeping to England, there is no real evidence of this. It is likely that the dovecotes or aviaries were constructed of wood, and have not stood the test of time. Early Christians and traders such as the Phoenicians coming to Cornwall for tin, would have played a part, and there was also a Saint Columba who had connections with Cornwall. There are two parish churches named after him, St. Columb Major and St. Columb Minor. (Columba is Latin for dove or pigeon).

But it was the Normans, the religious orders again mainly from France like the Benedictines, and a little later the Crusaders, who would have seen the huge pigeon towers in the Middle East, and who were the first to build substantial colonies of pigeons in this country. The reason for this interest in pigeon keeping was mainly culinary. There is a reference to the Stock dove being kept by monks, but pigeons would have played an important part in any community's diet, along with fish and rabbits. Game was very much the prerogative of the Royal family and nobility, and fresh meat was difficult to come by at certain times of the year. Livestock agriculture was still in a very primitive form; most beasts were killed in the autumn as there was no fodder to take them through the winter. The meat would have been salted, so fresh young pigeons would have made a welcome addition to the diet.

By the 1500's through to the 1800's dovecotes had become very fashionable, with every aspiring landowner building one, often reflecting the style or architecture of the region or period. It is interesting to see the number of Scottish dovecotes or doocotes that reflect a French influence. These dovecotes were the scourge of the peasant farmers, and many a conflict arose between the local landlord (owner of the dovecote), and the nearby peasant farmer. In France there was a more equitable solution, as before a landlord could build a dovecote, he had to own a minimum of 50 cultivated acres around it. It is thought that in the 1600's there were about 26,000 pigeon houses in this country, but the number could have been greater as in 1862 in the french Haute-Garonne department near Toulouse there were no less than 430,000! Certainly if you go down to that part of France, masses can be seen, and in fact there is a complete new culture of interest in pigeon houses developing over there, with books, postcards and models of the various kinds and styles that are to be found.

Sadly today many of these dovecotes are in a state of decay, but there is also a new found interest in England, and more and more dovecotes are being 'saved'. One interesting point is that most of them were built away from the main farmyard so that the pigeons would not foul the animals' water or food there; it also gave the pigeons, which were semi-feral and very nervous, a little peace. Today the feral pigeon has been replaced by the Collared dove which nests in barns, much to the chagrin of the modern farmer. There are incentives to keep all forms of wildlife out of farm buildings, particularly storage areas.

In 1998, Sara and I undertook a study tour of Egypt, looking at birds in domestication. One of our principle studies was pigeon keeping and here are some extracts from my notes:

Today in Egypt there are many pigeon towers for the tourists to see as they glide past in their air conditioned coaches. Some of these towers are built on top of blocks of flats or houses but most are built in the fields singly or in clusters as in the Fayoum area. They come in many different shapes and sizes but in the northern area of Egypt there are two main types: the Fayoum design which looks like a castle with sticks pointing out in all directions, and the Delta design which is a round conical tower of which there are many variations.

A bas-relief showing doves in a cage or box from the mastaba of Mereruka, Saqqara (Circa 2200 BC).

I was pleased to discover that the Egyptians are still constructing these towers, which last between 20-40 years depending on earthquakes. I was even more pleased to meet a man who builds them and to learn how it is done. Most of today's towers are built on plinths of concrete, and come in two sizes, 4 metre and 10 metre diameter, but this is subject to variation. The 4 metre diameter towers are 10 metres high, and the 10 metre towers are 20 metres high, (65 feet). The base of the tower is normally round, (but we did see some square ones), and they have a small access door on one side. The doors today are all metal with a sliding bolt fastener, but the older towers had wooden doors. The material used in the construction is mud and straw, about 5 cubic metres of mud to 100 kilos of chopped straw. Earthenware vessels and tubes are set in this mixture to form the walls. The vessels and the tubes slope upwards and inwards, and are placed row upon row. The reason for the slope is to stop rain getting inside the tower and to prevent the pigeon eggs from rolling out when the bird leaves the nest; the tubes allow access from outside and also ventilation. They are set into the walls in varying geometric designs, and like the vessels, are approximately 8" (20 cms) in diameter. Inside the tower there are wooden planks or beams crossing from one side to the other, set at intervals of a metre up the walls. These allow first of all for the construction of the tower, and secondly for the harvesting of the young pigeons. The birds use these beams to perch on as well. As the tower grows, sticks or pieces of wood are stuck into the outside to allow the pigeons to land.

Once the tower is completed and the sides smoothed off, it is then painted, usually white to reflect the heat of the sun; sometimes bands of blue and red are also added. The smooth sides are important to keep rats and snakes out. Inside, the overwhelming impression is of a huge honeycomb; they are wonderfully cool too. I did see the body of a hawk hanging outside from one of the sticks in the Fayoum area, which I presume was a deterant to any other hawks.

Sometimes pigeons are introduced from other colonies, but these towers are colonised mainly by feral pigeons. Any extra male pigeons tend to bring in spare females and so the pigeon tower builds up. The pigeons are virtually self sufficient, feeding from the surrounding fields and back yards. A supplementary diet of maize is fed around the base of the tower during February, March and April when the pickings are poor, before the harvest. Once the colony is up to strength, about 1,000 pairs in a 20 metre tower, the young squabs are harvested providing an income of about $1,500 (1998) per annum. Each pair of pigeons in the tower will produce two squabs every 40 days, and have between 5 - 7 hatches over a nine month period, so approximately 12,000 squabs are produced each year. Pigeon meat is eaten extensively in Egypt and used to be a main source of avian protein before the new factory chicken farms arrived. Pigeons produced by these traditional methods in towers seem to be disease free. The main breeds used are Kattawi and Balidi, and some imports known as Malti and Berri, all of which come in a variety of colours.

The main by-product from these towers is manure which the Egyptians use on their land or gardens. One of the chief reasons why pigeon houses and dovecotes were built so extensively across Europe in the Middle Ages was obviously to provide meat. What is not so widely known is that the by-product manure was equally valuable for two reasons: it contained saltpetre which first of all is the main component of gunpowder (75% saltpetre, 15% charcoal, 10% sulphur), and secondly, is used for curing leather. We discovered this while researching in Morocco; the tanneries which are attached to most of the larger towns, buy in pigeon manure to use in one of the first processes of curing hides, mainly sheep and goats and the odd camel as well. The hides are immersed in evil smelling pits containing pigeon manure and water and left to soak for 7 - 10 days; from this we get beautiful Moroccan bindings on books!

For a matter of interest here is a comparison of various farmyard manures in percentage values of organic fertilisers.

	Nitrogen	Potash	Phosphorus
pig manure	0.49	0.35	0.58
cow manure	0.45	0.04	0.11
poultry manure	1.68	0.49	0.90
pigeon manure	5.85	1.76	2.09

So you can see why pigeon manure is so highly prized.

THE DECLINE OF THE DOVECOTE

The decline in keeping pigeons in large dovecotes started towards the end of the 1800's and continued until the 1920's when they ceased to be used. There were several factors that caused this.

By the end of the 1700's and into the 1800's, larger farms started to emerge, and were being managed professionally. This was due in part to the decline of the big estates and the industrialisation of Britain, which saw many people leaving the country for the towns and cities. Transport was becoming more organised with better roads and the appearance of the railways; this meant that farm produce could be delivered quickly, hence there was less need for country communities to be self-sufficient as farming methods improved. There was also the age-old curse of his Lordship's pigeons damaging nearby crops. By this time fresh meat was available throughout the year, and birds like geese, turkeys and hens were beginning to be sold in large numbers.

The other main reason for the decline in pigeon keeping was the advance in shot gun technology bringing with it a change from just shooting for food with a single ball muzzle-loaded gun, to shooting for sport with a breech loaded gun and cartridges. This meant that guns could be reloaded quickly and in some cases two or three guns could be used by one person, particularly during game shooting. When the game shooting season was over, pigeon shooting started to become popular. The problem was there were not enough birds to cater for this sport, and many pigeons were stolen from dovecotes at night to fulfill a need. However, eventually 'clay' pigeons were invented. The early ones were glass spheres filled with feathers or coloured powder, but gradually round saucer-shaped projectiles took over as they were easier to make and could fly over 60 yards. It is interesting to note that the French call clay pigeon shooting 'ball trap', ball coming from the glass spheres and trap from the time when pigeons were released from traps or boxes.

In recent times pigeon has more or less ceased to play a part in the British diet, but in France people still rear squabs for the table, using mainly breeds such as Kings and Carneau. When pigeon is eaten in the countryside today it is usually Woodpigeon, but there is a problem with this: you can't be sure of the age of the bird, so your acorn-packing, sprout-feeding, rape-gorging Woodpigeon can be fairly solid going; it was always said that if you ate Woodpigeon for seven days on the trot, you would die of indigestion! During the Second World War, feral pigeons were caught in London, to improve the diet and menu of the Londoners, but these birds had to be cooked very slowly in order to make them at all edible!

Although large dovecotes are now no longer used, polecotes and wallcotes are becoming popular these days as decorative features, and more and more people are discovering the joys of keeping a few birds to enhance their gardens. From being kept solely as a source of food for thousands of years, pigeons and doves are now giving many people much pleasure, as they soar over the lawns and trees or strut and preen in their aviaries.

This is a pillared dovecote, near Marssac, Albi, showing the beauty of some of these regional dovecotes in France. This one has a Cow's Tail roof.

LIST OF VETERINARY SURGEONS

ENGLAND

AVON
J.R. Best, The Vet Surgery, 32 West Hill, PORTISHEAD, Bristol, BS20 9LN
Tel - 01275 847400   Avian
                                     P.M.'s

BERKSHIRE
Mr. S.W. Cooke, Avian & Exotic Vet. Centre, Kelperland Vet. Group, Ascot Road, Touchenend, MAIDENHEAD, Berkshire, SL6 3LA
Tel - 01628 24935   Spec. interest in poultry
                                     Avian
                                     P.M.'s

CAMBS
K. Gooderham, Marsh Lane, Hemingford Grey, HUNTINGDON, Cambs PE18 9EN
Tel - 01480 62816   Spec. interest in poultry
                                     Avian
                                     P.M.'s

CHESHIRE
Ian Cameron, Manor Court Vet. Centre, Church St, TARVIN, Cheshire, CH2 8EB
Tel - 01829 40639   Unsure

B. Coles, Cranmore Vet. Centre, 140 Chester Road, CHILDER THORNTON, Wirral, Cheshire, L66 1QN
Tel - 0151 339 9141   Spec. interest in poultry
                                     Avian
                                     P.M.'s

DEVON
Mrs. S. Lewis-Jones, 5 High Street, HONITON, Devon
Tel - 01404 42657   Avian
                                     P.M.'s

D.J. Shingleton, Waterman Farm, Ugborough, IVYBRIDGE, S.Devon, PL21 0PB
Tel - 01548 830552   Spec. interest in poultry
                                     Avian
                                     P.M.'s

Mr. R. Turner, St. David's Vet. Group, Marsh Barton Farm, Clyst St. George, EXETER, EX3 0QH
Tel - 01392 876622   Spec. interest in poultry
                            P.M.'s

DORSET
Mr. T.M. Phillips, St Marys Vet. Clinic, 300 Ringwood Road, FERNDOWN, BH22 8DX
Tel - 01202 876901   Avian

ESSEX
M.P. Lawton, 12 Fitzilian Ave, Harold Wood, ROMFORD, Essex, RM3 0QS
Tel - 01708 384444   Avian
                            P.M.'s

Blackwater Vet. Group, Lion Cottage, Maypole Road, TIPTREE, Colchester, CO5 0EJ
Tel 01206 818282   Avian
                            P.M.'s

H. Hellig & Partners, 14 Church Lane, COLCHESTER, CO3 4AF
Tel - 01206 48516   Spec. interest in poultry
                            Avian
                            P.M.'s

GLOS
R.W. Blowey, Glos. Labs, St Oswalds Road, GLOUCESTER, GL1 2SJ
Tel - 01452 524961   Spec. interest in poultry
                            Avian
                            P.M.'s

R.S. Broadbent, Stow Vet. Surgns, Backwalls, STOW-ON-THE-WOLD, GL54 1DS
Tel - 01451 830620   Specs. interest in poultry
                            Avian
                            P.M.'s

N.A. Forbes, The Clock House Vet. Hosp, Wallbridge, STROUD, Glos, GL5 3JD
Tel - 01453 672555   Spec. interest in poultry
                            Avian
                            P.M.'s

HAMPSHIRE
Mr. P.W. Scott, Keanter, Stoke Charity Road, Kings Worthy, WINCHESTER, SO23 7LS
Tel - 01962 883895   Avian
                                  P.M.'s

HEREFORD
P.W. Laing, 40 Etnam Street, LEOMINSTER, Herefordshire, HR6 8AQ
Tel - 01568 613232   Spec. in poultry & game birds
                                  Avian
                                  P.M.'s

Mrs. S.E. Pattison, Westmoor Veterinary Services, Mortimer Cottage, Westmoor, MANSEL LACY, Hereford, HR4 7HN
Tel - 01981 590603   Spec. in poultry & game birds
                                  P.M.'s

HERTS
Heath Lodge Vet. Group, St Bernard's Road, ST. ALBANS, Herts, AL3 5RA
Tel - 01727 835294   Spec. in poultry
                                  Avian
                                  P.M.'s

LANCS
Mr. A.P. Raftery. 221 Upper Chorlton Road, MANCHESTER, M16 0DE
Tel - 0161 881 6868   Avian
                                  P.M.'s

S.M.F. Jennings, Manchester Street Vet. Surg, Manchester Street, OLDHAM, OL8 1UF
Tel - 0161 624 4596   Avian
                                  P.M.'s

Alan Pearson, Morningside, 30 Bonds Lane, GARSTANG, Preston
Tel - 01995 24599   Unsure

LEICS
Meadow Lane Vet. Centre, 9 Meadow Lane, LOUGHBOROUGH, Leics, LE11 1JU
Tel - 01509 212437   Avian
                                  P.M.'s

LINCOLNSHIRE
C. Harding, Horncastle Lab. Southwell Lane, HORNCASTLE, Lincs, LN9 5DT
Tel - 01507 523276   Spec. in poultry
                                  P.M.'s

LONDON
K.A. Whitcomb, 14 Portland Road, LONDON, W11
Tel - 0171 727 2204   Poultry - interest in no specialist qual.
                                Avian
                                P.M.'s

C. Hall, 15 Temple Sheen Road, SHEEN, SW14 7PX
Tel - 0181 876 9696   Avian
                                P.M.'s

NORFOLK
G.R. Duncan, Large Animal Office, 40 Yarmouth Road, NORTH WALSHAM, NR28 9AT
Tel - 01692 407040   Spec. in poultry
                                Avian
                                P.M.'s

S.A. Lister BSc B.Vet.Med. MRCVS. J Saverzapf, Chapelfield Vet. Partnership, McLintock House, 21 Chapelfield Road, NORWICH, NR2 1RR
Tel - 01603 629046/7/8/9   Spec. in poultry
                                Avian
                                P.M.'s

OXON
Aylmer & Cannon, Vet. Hospital, Albion Street, CHIPPING NORTON, Oxon, OX7 5BN
Tel - 01608 642547   Spec. in poultry
                                Avian
                                P.M.'s

SOMERSET
A.J. Parsons, Tower Hill Road, CREWKERNE, Somerset, TA18 8EQ
Tel - 01460 72443   Avian
                                P.M.'s

SUSSEX
O. Swarbrick, Denmans Lane, Fontwell, ARUNDEL, Sussex, BN18 0SU
Tel - 01243 682300   Spec. in poultry
                                Avian
                                P.M.'s

D.C. Lang, Cliffe Vet. Group, 21 Cliffe High Street, LEWES, E Sussex, BN7 2AH
Tel - 01273 473232   Avian
                                P.M.'s

Howe & Starnes, Fairfield House, UCKFIELD, E Sussex, TN22 5DE
Tel - 01825 764268   Spec. interest in poultry
                           Avian
                           P.M.'s

WARKS

S.D.J. Marston, 94/6 King Street, BEDWORTH, Warks, CV12 8JF
Tel - 01203 312193   Deal with poultry
                           Avian

WILTS

D.G. Parsons, 10 Indus Acre, Avro Way, Bowerhill, MELKSHAM, Wilts,
SN12 6TP
Tel - 01225 790090   Spec. in poultry
                           Avian
                           P.M.'s

WORCS

J.C. Waine, 97 Mount Pleasant, REDDITCH, Worcs, B97 4JD
Tel - 01527 550111   Avian
                           P.M.'s

YORKSHIRE

A.G. Greenwood, Int. Zoo Vet. Grp, Keighley Bus. Centre, South Street,
KEIGHLEY, W Yorks, BD21 1AG
Tel - 01535 692000   Avian

Mr. G. Grant, The Vet. Surgery, Salisbury Road, YORK, YO2 4YN
Tel - 01904 643997   Spec. interest in poultry
                           Avian
                           P.M.'s

WALES

GWYNEDD

E Barbour-Hill, Tan y Coed, Penlon, High Street, BANGOR, Gwynedd,
LL57 1PX
Tel - 01248 355674   Avian interest
                           P.M.'s

Tudor Lawson & Dallimore, Bala Road, DOLGELLAU, Gwynedd, LL40 2YF
Tel - 01341 422212   Avian
                           P.M.'s

CLWYD

Dr John Baker, The Dormie, Bertha-Dou, RHOSEMOR, Clwyd, CH7 6PS
Tel - 01352 780307   P.M.'s on cage birds only

John Parry Hickerton, Rhianfa Vet. Centre, 83 Russell Road, RHYL, Clwyd, LL18 3DR
Tel - 01745 332553   Spec. in poultry
                            Avian
                            P.M.'s

SCOTLAND

ABERDEENSHIRE
Laurence T.A. Brain, The Vet. Clinic, 36 High Street, New Deer, TURRIFF, Aberdeenshire, AB53 6SX
Tel - 01771 644205   P.M.'s

EDINBURGH
G.J. Waterall, Almond Vet. Centre, 89 Colinton Road, EDINBURGH, EH10 5DF
Tel - 0131 337 1471   Avian

AYR
Mr. Tom Pennycott, SAC Vet. Services, Avian Health Unit, AUCHINCRUIVE, Ayr, KA6 5AE
Tel - 01292 520318   Spec. in poultry
                            Avian
                            P.M.'s

FIFE
W.A. Law, Inchcolm Vet. Services, 36 The Wynd, DALGETY BAY, Fife, KY11 5SJ
Tel - 01383 823178   Spec. in poultry

WE ARE ALWAYS DELIGHTED TO HEAR FROM ANY AVIAN VETS WHO HAVE NOT BEEN INCLUDED ON THIS LIST

These are two pigeon houses I constructed for our garden in Devon.

67

Two examples of Mules Foot dovecotes so typical in the area around Toulouse in France. These were probably the last pigeon houses to be built in any number, and were functional rather than attractive. If you look carefully you will see terra-cotta pigeon-shaped finials on the roof. These are called stool pigeons and help to attract birds to the dovecote.

PUBLICATIONS:

Feathered World -   5 Winckley Street, Preston, PR1 2AA
                               Tel - 01772 250246
                               (mostly non racing or fancy breeds)

British Homing World   c/o The Royal Pigeon Racing
                               Association, The Reddings, Nr
                               Cheltenham, Glos, GL51 6RN
                               Tel - 01452 713529
                               (Racing Pigeon News)
                               Internet: www.pigeonracing.com.

PIGEON EQUIPMENT & ACCESSORIES

Boddy & Ridewood, Eastfield Ind Estate, Scarborough, North Yorkshire,
YO11 3UY
Tel: 01723 585858
Internet: www.pigeons.co.uk

Interhatch, 27 Derbyshire Lane, Sheffield, S8 9EH
Tel: 0114 255 2340 or 6622

S & A Pigeon Supplies Ltd., Silk & Terry House, Warstock Road, Warstock,
Birmingham B14 4RS
Tel: 0121 4746741

POLECOTES & WALLCOTES

Forsham Cottage Arks
Goreside Farm, Great Chard, Ashford, Kent, TN26 1JU
Tel: 01233 820229

King Dovecotes
75 Copthorne Road, Felbridge,East Grinstead, Sussex, RH19 2PB
Tel: 01342 324159 Fax: 01342 315228

Kootensaw Dovecotes
Oakwood, The Cider Works, Chudleigh, Newton Abbot, TQ13 0EL
Tel/Fax: 01626 854999

Shropshire Dovecotes
54, Wallshead Way, Church Aston, Newport, Shropshire TF10 9LR
Tel - 01952 810080

W.G.F. Dovecotes
Laburnums, Church Road, Wreningham, Norwich NR16 1BA
Tel - 01508 489347

LOST RACING PIGEONS

The Royal Pigeon Racing Association
The Reddings, Near Cheltenham, Glos, GL51 6RN
Tel - 01452 713529

SHOWS -   For lists of Fancy Pigeon shows see Feathered World
For Racing pigeon or Homing pigeon shows contact
The Royal Pigeon Racing Ass.

BREEDERS

Feathered World
contains a list of many breeders of all kinds of pigeons and doves.

National Pigeon Association, c/o Mrs Tracey Edwards, Bridge Villa, Main Street, Pollington, Goole. DN14 0DW. Tel: 01405 869516 For information on breeds and breeders.

I have included a few breeders who have been very helpful and who I am sure would help you as well.

David Brown	01424 813464
(East Sussex)	(White Garden Fantails only)
Pat Pratt	01235 868 869
(Near Wantage)	(12 breeds)
Mr. Beer	01752 845469
(Near Plymouth)	(4 Breeds)

PIGEON BOOKS (new and old)

Veronica Mayhew, Trewena, Behoes Lane, Woodcote, Nr Reading, RG8 0PP.
Tel - 01 491 680 743

TERROR EYES for Pigeons' wings

Dazer International, 204 Broadway, Peterborough, PE1 4DT
Tel - 01 733 315 888
Fax - 01 733 555 848

This is an arcade-type dovecote, near Fanjeaux, Carcassonne, recently restored.

A round dovecote, now incorporated into the house, at Baisseriette, near Castres, France.

71

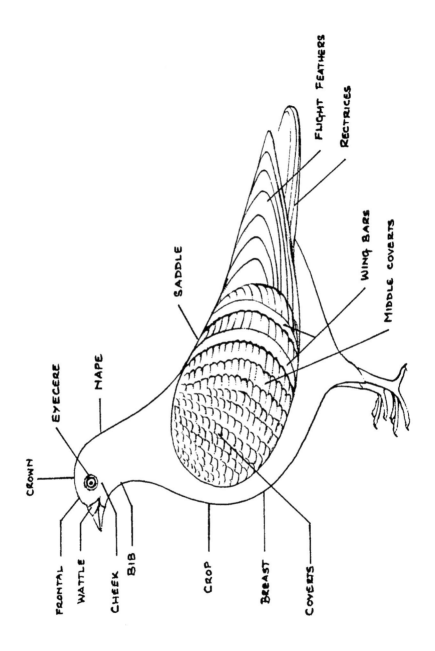

CROWN

EYECERE

NAPE

SADDLE

FLIGHT FEATHERS

RECTRICES

WING BARS

MIDDLE COVERTS

FRONTAL

WATTLE

CHEEK

BIB

CROP

BREAST

COVERTS

PIGEON TERMINOLOGY

argent - applied to Modenas having a white centre on the coloured feather. Their ground colour is white. The colour effect of argent Modenas is similar to that of the Silverlaced Wyandotte chickens.

badge - pigeon with coloured body and white wing tips.

band - identification ring on pigeon's legs

barred - having bands of alternate colours running across the feather

barrel - frontal between the eye and the beak-wattle, as in medium-faced Antwerps

bay - yellow-orange colour in eyes

beard - white feathers below beak of coloured pigeons

beetle-browed - cere above eye leaning over

bell-neck - coloured markings on back of neck against white background

bib - patch of coloured feathers below beak of white pigeons

bishoped - white shoulder patches or wing-edgings of such shoulder-marked varieties as Oriental Frills and Turbits; a fault

blocky - having broad, substantial build

bloom - gloss, sheen, or finish on plumage

body - trunk of pigeon

bolting eye - prominent eye, as in Turbits

booted - feathered on shanks and toes

box-beak - close fitting beak, as in Carriers and other stout-beaked breeds

breed - race, variety, kind, sort

breeding down - process of producing small specimens

broken-coloured - having two or more colours

73

broken-eyed - lacking uniform colour of eyes

brows - skull projections over eyes

bull-eye - eye with dark-coloured iris; also called "black" eye

cap - head markings of such varieties as Swallows

caruncles - irregular and other more or less abnormal growths of flesh about eyes and over nostrils

carriage - general bearing of pigeon

chain - fore-part of frill, as in Jacobins

checkered - having wing feathers with irregularly coloured tips. Black-checkered feathers are black tipped with blue, blue-checkered feathers are blue tipped with black: etc

clean-legged - having no feathers on shanks or feet

close-feathered - having feathers lying flat against body; same as "tight-feathered"

cobby - heavily, solidly built, more or less round in form

cock - male pigeon

condition (noun) - quality of pigeon as regards state of health and of plumage

condition (verb) - to wash, tame, train, or otherwise prepare a pigeon for show room

cream - yellowish-white

crest - feather tuft at back-skull. If it extends across the head, it is called "shell-crest"; if it terminates in a point, then it is called a "pin-crest"

crop - pouchlike enlargement of gullet, in which food is stored and softened before it is passed into gizzard

cushion - excessive quantity of soft feathers about tail

deep-bodied - having noticeable depth of body from top of back to lower side of breastbone

TOP. Dovecot Street; in France references to pigeons or pigeon houses are to be found everywhere, from street names to the names of places, villages and towns.

ABOVE. A carved wooden relief in an Abbey showing doves drinking from a fountain. The Abbey, Caunes-Minervois.

75

dewlap - growth of loose skin below the beak

dominant - traits or characteristics which predominate in breeding

double-lacing - pencilling of outer edge of feather, as in Oriental Frills

dove - any specimen of the smaller species of pigeons

down-faced - having full frontal and sloping beak, as in Owls

faking - using unfair means to put pigeons in show condition, as removing or dyeing objectionable feathers and similar practices

family - strain

feeders - pigeons used as foster parents to raise young of the short-beaked varieties

flight-coverts - short feathers growing at the base of the flight feathers, which they cover in part

flights or flight feathers - primary feathers on wings

fluff - down part of feather; also, profuse soft feathering about thighs and abdomen

foreign colour - colour not belonging to variety according to standard

foul feathers - feathers of a colour not belonging to variety

frill - fluffed feathers on throat, as in Oriental Frills and Turbits

frog headed - having depression between eyes over crown of skull as in Turbits

Gazzi - Modenas having white bodies, but coloured heads, wings, and tails

globe - air filled, circular throat, as in Pouters

grizzle - mixture of blue and white in a sort of "salt and pepper" effect, especially around the head and neck

hackle - long, flowing feathers growing on neck of pigeons

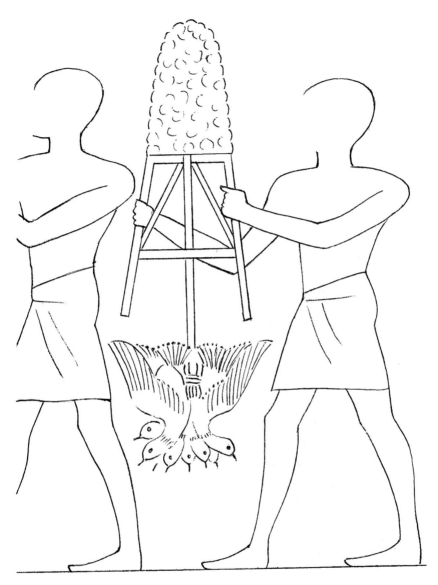

A bas-relief from a temple at Dendera circa 45 BC, showing trussed pigeons (probably Turtle doves).

handkerchief - mottling of white feathers on scapular plumage of such varities as Mottled Tumblers

hen - female pigeon

hock - joint between thigh and shank

homing - faculty of returning to home loft over territory, which is at least in part new or strange to flyer

hood - inverted feathers on neck, as in Jacobin

inbreeding - mating closely related birds to each other, as father to daughter, brother to sister, etc

keel - lower edge of breastbone

kit - a number of pigeons, such as Rollers or Tipplers, trained to fly together

lacing - marginal edging of a feather; usually darker than the body of the feather

larking - triangular brown or black patches on wings

leggy - having legs too long

line breeding - modified inbreeding from a certain number of birds not too closely related, such as mating daughter to father or son to mother, according to a definite plan

Magnani - Modenas whose plumage has a dappled or spangled effect, by virtue of a mixture of several colours

mandibles - horny, upper and lower portions of beak or bill

mane - rear part of Jacobin's frill

markings - lacing, barring, striping, or any other kind of marks on plumage

mealy - powdery silver with red bars; colour of meal

mottled - having small, crescent-shaped patches of white on a ground plumage of a single or "self" colour

78

A delightful dovecote, recently restored, in a garden at Carlus near Albi. Note the pigeon access holes, made from one piece of stone.

muff - growth of feathers on shanks or toes

outcross - using a pigeon of a different strain for breeding purposes

peeper - squab ready to leave the nest

pied - (adj.) - having one colour splashed with patches of feathers of a different colour; applied particularly to coloured birds with patches of white

pigeon milk - soft, white substance secreted by crop and fed to newly hatched squabs for some days

pinch-eyed - having slight narrowness at rear part of otherwise round eye-cere of Dragoon

pin-crest - see crest

primaries - flight feathers

racy - applied to a slender, trim, tight feathered bird of alert carriage

roach back - hump back

rose - centre of the rosette forming the frill of the Jacobin; white feathers appearing on the shoulders of certain varieties, such as Pouters, in the shape of a rose; a compact group of feathers, radiating from the centre of the skull, as in Trumpeters

rose-wing - having several white feathers near the centre of each wing; applied only to solidly coloured birds

Ruff - a name for the Jacobin

saddle - that portion of the back extending between the transverse median line of the back and the base of the tail

scaly leg - mite-disease of the shanks and feet

Schietti - applied to Modenas, meaning coloured all over, regardless of kind of colour. Classification includes white self-coloured

secondaries - the long quill feathers of the wings, growing next to and above the primaries

self-colour - any uniform or solid colour

A modern concrete pigeon tree house, at a stoneware factory at Gaiarin near Albi.

shank - that portion of the leg between the toes and the hock joint

sheath - the covering of a new feather. It splits and falls off as the feather develops

shell-crest - see crest

shoeing - the feathers below the main tail feathers; especially noticeable in Fantails

short-faced - having very short beak and frontal, as in Turbits and Owls

shoulder - front, or upper part of the wing

silver - very delicate shade of blue with a little cream

slipped wing - a wing with twisted or improperly folding secondaries

smooth-legged - having legs without feathers, stubs, or down on the shanks

smut - dark colouring superimposed on some other and usually standard colour

snip - patch of white or coloured feathers above beak

solid colour - one colour throughout

spangled - dark marking at the tip of a feather

spindle-beak - thin or pointed beak

splashed - having uneven markings (colour and white); sometimes called stippled

split-eyed - having the iris partly black and partly bright coloured

sport - sudden spontaneous variation from type or breed; a mutation

squeaker - squab ready to leave the nest; especially applied to young racing homers

stippled - see splashed

stock birds - pigeons withdrawn from racing and from showing and used solely for breeding

I was getting fed up with the food container's lid blowing off and the food getting wet, so I designed a revolving feeder which turned in the wind. This was a prototype and it worked well, but it did take a little time before the doves enjoyed the ride!

stockings - short feathers covering the lower joint and claws of such varieties as the frillbacks and the Ancients

stop - an indentation causing an angular appearance between a projecting beak and a rising forehead; as in the short faced Tumbler

strain - birds of one variety bred in line for a definite purpose for five or more generations from a certain number of foundation birds

stud - collection of pure-bred birds

team - four pigeons on exhibition: a pair of old birds and a pair of youngsters

thighs - upper segment of the leg

throat - same as gullet

ticked - having plumage with spots of colour different from that of the remainder of the plumage

toy - small pigeon bred only for markings, such as the Ice or the Crescent

trap - bob-wire door through which pigeon can enter but not leave loft

trimming - preparation of pigeons for exhibition

tucked up - applied to wings held up nicely; not drooping

type - form or carriage peculiar to a certain variety

Twerp - racing pigeon fanciers from Antwerp who continually released birds that never returned to their loft. Circa 1925

utility - bred for squab production, not fancy or exhibition purposes

whiskered - smooth continuation of reversed frill feathering, beginning at breast and running to sides of head

wing-bar - a broad stripe of colour usually different from that of the remainder of the plumage, running across the wings

wing-coverts - feathers covering the roots of the secondary flight feathers